D1255999

SKY RANGERS

Books by Eloise Engle

SKY RANGERS: *Satellite Tracking Around the World*
    (*with Kenneth H. Drummond*)
PARARESCUE: *What Men Dare Do*
ESCAPE: *From the Air and From the Sea*

SKY RANGERS

Satellite Tracking Around the World

Eloise Engle and

Kenneth H. Drummond

ILLUSTRATED

The John Day Company   New York

PHOTOGRAPH CREDITS
Bendix Corporation: p. 150; British Central Office of Information: p. 131;
Hughes Aircraft Company: p. 177; National Aeronautics and Space Administration: pp. 12, 13, 16, 47, 50, 53, 55, 63, 82, 88, 105, 170, 173, 175, 179,
181, 188, 194, 196, 197, 198, 201, 203, 204; North American Air Defense
Command: pp. 115, 117, 118, 121, 135, 145, 146; RCA: pp. 128, 129, 132,
133, 136, 140, 142; Smithsonian Astrophysical Observatory: pp. 72, 75, 77,
80, 85, 91, 95, 97; United States Air Force: pp. 18, 20, 127; United States
Navy: pp. 31, 43, 159, 163, 164.

Acknowledgments

THE birth of a book idea is very exciting. A writer never knows quite when it will happen or where the impetus will strike. But suddenly a word here, an idea there, will start the wheels turning. Once begun, there is no forgetting a story of this sort. The helpless writer is swept along, intrigued and curious and certainly admiring the people who play the major roles in the true-life drama.

This book all began with a casual conversation with Ken Drummond, its coauthor. He told me of the early days of the International Geophysical Year (IGY) when he was associated with the Smithsonian Astrophysical Observatory (SAO) and related some of the difficulties encountered in setting up the optical tracking stations. Ken, who is a leading oceanographer, was experienced in the personnel selection and logistics for isolated areas and was therefore sought after for administrative work in establishing optical satellite tracking stations in foreign countries. Aha, thought I, we have a first-hand account of how the optical tracking systems for satellites were really set up. Experts from other tracking systems could be called on for help. We have a book!

Our credits are many and varied and many of them interlock. Ken, who has personally inspected many of the worldwide tracking stations, received marvelous cooperation and help from Dr. Fred L. Whipple, Director, SAO, Cambridge, Massachusetts; Dr. Luigi Jacchia, astrophysicist, Harvard College observatory; Mr. E. Nelson Hayes, technical writer,

5

SAO; Dr. John B. White, Publications, SAO; Dr. J. Allen Hynek, Director, Dearborn Observatory, Evanston, Illinois; Mr. Walter Lang, Texas A and M University; Mr. E. C. Buckley, Director Office of Tracking and Data Acquisition, NASA (National Aeronautics and Space Administration); Dr. Martin Burkhead, University of Wisconsin; Mr. Richard M. Adams of the U.S. Oceanographic Office; and Mr. C. M. Peterson, Chief of Communications, SAO, Cambridge, Massachusetts.

I am particularly indebted to interviewees who gave freely of their time: Dr. John Hagen, former Director of Project Vanguard; Dr. Paul Walsh, his Deputy Director of the Project; Admiral Rossen Bennet who was Chief of Naval Research during the IGY. Roger Easton, Captain Winfred Berg, Martin Votaw, and David Saltus all added their special notes to the book. Mike Harloff, who is now with NASA, furnished many tips and ideas based on his experiences with Project Vanguard.

Research trips took me to Blossom Point, Maryland, where Minitrack people rolled out the red carpet. At Dahlgren, Virginia (Space Surveillance), the Navy did its utmost to explain the complicated manner in which "silent" satellites are tracked today. A thrilling experience was a trip to NORAD (North American Air Defense Command) where I gathered material on tracking for defense. My special thanks go to Lieutenant Colonel Milt Kegley and others in the Department of Defense for arranging this important mission.

Ed Mason and Jim Lacy at Goddard Space Flight Center, Maryland, have been enormously helpful throughout the project. I have leaned heavily on the historical volume, *The Early Years*, NASA, 1964.

ELOISE ENGLE

Falls Church, Virginia

Contents

SKY RANGERS

1

Satellite Tracking Around the World

FIVE, four, three, two, one. IGNITION! MAIN-STAGE! LIFT-OFF!

This is the heart-stopping moment when to most people, success or failure of a space shot hangs in the balance. Will it be a "go" or "no-go"? Will months of labor and millions of dollars explode in a fiery pyre? And even more terrible, if the spacecraft is manned, will human life be swallowed up in the raging inferno?

The rocket's propellants suddenly ignite in a giant spectrum of color. Deafening thunderclaps explode across the quiet land as the sleek bird struggles to move upward into the sky. It hovers for a split second in the midst of billowing white vapor, but as fuel is consumed, it picks up speed. The second stage is ignited. There is a mighty burst of acceleration. At burnout of the final stage, the vehicle is inserted into orbit.

The hushed silence after the satellite or spacecraft has disappeared from view is an eerie contrast to the soul-

Five, Four, Three, Two, One. IGNITION! MAINSTAGE! LIFT-OFF! This is the heart-stopping moment when, to most people, success or failure of a space shot hangs in the balance. Shown here is Explorer X, launched at Cape Kennedy.

For hundreds of satellite trackers at their ground stations around
the world, the show has just begun. Shown here is a sky ranger
manning the 85-foot-diameter radar antenna used in the tracking of
spacecraft designed for flyby orbit and landing on the moon and
other planets.

shaking fireworks that have just gone on. A vapor trail wafts
crazily into antic patterns; birds, crickets, and insects resume
their strangely incongruous chorus.

Well, that's that.

Across the nation television sets are switched off. It is
time to go to the office, or to the kitchen to finish the dishes.
The show is over; there is other work to be done. Back to
the books at school and other homely earthbound duties.

Surely the shot was successful. The bird got up there didn't it? We can all stand a bit taller and smile proudly at this latest triumph of our space experts. And while we go about our business, somebody, somewhere, will undoubtedly keep track of it. It seems too much of an anticlimax to worry about a satellite once it has attained the desired orbit.

But for hundreds of satellite trackers at their ground stations around the world, the show has just begun. They know that the whole point of the shot is to find out what is going on up there, beyond the earth's enveloping atmosphere. Not for them the glamour, action, and drama of the countdown and lift-off, although their hearts beat a little faster as their TV monitors tell them the crucial moment approaches. Their teletypes click frantically as reams of yellow paper with black printing spew out; electronic gear hums with data it is digesting; and like the rest of the world, these sky rangers wonder if the shot will succeed. But to satellite trackers, and to the general public, success means two quite different things.

For instance, success to a tracker means that he has quickly determined the trajectory (angle) of the rocket as it left the pad. In a manned flight, he would have had only a few seconds in which to make his pronouncement as to whether an abort was necessary. Had a scientific satellite veered off course, the designated tracker would have calmly pushed the "destruct" button. Fortunately, according to the trackers' electronic eyes and ears, this shot behaved beautifully.

Now that the vehicle is in orbit, what happens next?

In a manned flight, the tracker must make sure the astronaut is in voice contact at all times with the scientists on the ground. That vehicle, whizzing around the earth at thousands of miles per hour, over all sorts of terrain, over even uninhabited areas and oceans, must never be out of

Somebody has got to ride herd on the beeping, swirling, signaling satellites. Somebody has got to check their behavior as they loop around the globe in order to extract the valuable data they are collecting for earthbound scientists.

contact with its earthly guides. When it is time for him to return to earth and the brave astronaut waits for the signal to fire his retro-rockets, he knows his very life depends on the accuracy and dependability of the vast network of tracking stations below him. Forty-five minutes after he receives the word to fire his retro-rockets, he lands within a six-mile radius impact zone.

Tracking a manned flight is an exciting job. Human life is at stake. History is being made. Headlines will herald the feat in the morning paper. But what of the several hundred other objects in space that have been orbiting for years? Somebody has to ride herd on these beeping, twirling, signaling critters. Somebody has to check their behavior as they loop around the globe, in order to extract the valuable data they are collecting for earthbound scientists. Somebody has to command them so that they will continue to work for us. To do these jobs, trackers rely on "housekeeping telemetry."

This strange-sounding term describes how trackers, or sky

The Orbiting Solar Observatory (OSO) is the first of a series of large "second generation" spacecraft which will study the sun over at least one solar cycle (11 years). There are 13 scientific experiments on board OSO I, launched on March 7, 1962.

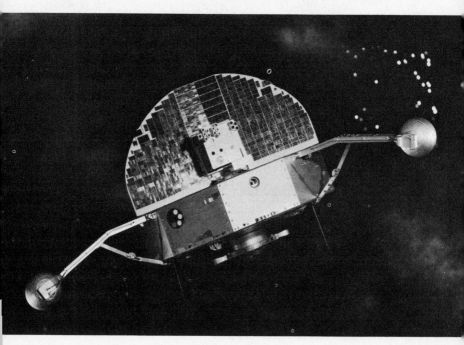

rangers as we have chosen to call them in this book, learn what happens to each and every scientific satellite in flight. And a lot does happen. Consider the drama taking place far beyond the limits of our earthly vision.

As if by magic, the satellite is out of its nose cone. Like a butterfly it comes out of its cocoon. In the case of the weather satellite Nimbus, huge shiny purple paddles called solar panels which measure the sun's rays unfold; stabilizing booms extend; antennas pop out like enormous toothpicks. Are all these prearranged maneuvers going according to schedule? Everything must be verified by the ground-based tracker. If there is trouble, scientists and engineers must know its cause in order not to make the same mistake again. Sometimes when something goes wrong, trackers can send commands to the satellite and correct the difficulty.

Edmund C. Buckley, Director of the Office of Tracking and Data Acquisition, National Aeronautics and Space Administration (NASA) explains, "We've had many satellites that were saved because of our trackers' ability to keep tabs on the bird. On one deep space probe, there was one diode (a vacuum tube with a cold anode and a heated cathode) in ten thousand that went wrong. Consequently all the numbers, which were actually messages from the satellite, were coming in wrong. This was mysterious because otherwise the satellite was behaving beautifully. Finally our men realized it was simply 'talking' in the wrong arithmetic language; adjustments were made at the ground stations to compensate for the differences and the satellite continued its productive voyage. In another case when we were tracking a deep probe, we learned that it was overheating, so we turned on the transmitters, which we hoped would have a cooling effect on the battery temperature. The trick worked, and the life of the vehicle was lengthened."

Such behind-the-scenes dramas never reach the headlines,

Outwardly, our sky rangers who keep a check on the growing list of satellites seem calm, nerveless, and businesslike. They must exercise constant self-discipline, for one wrong decision could be catastrophic. Shown here are T/Sgt. Gobby J. Sandefur (left), seated at the Antenna Control Board, and S/Sgt. Carl M. Golden, seated at the Radar and Tracking Control Board, at Kaena Point Tracking Station, Oahu, Hawaii.

but they demonstrate the kind of contributions made to space exploration by our satellite trackers. To them, a satellite or spacecraft is not just an impersonal piece of machinery tossed into orbit for the benefit of the scoreboard or the admiration of the public. Often, trackers are very well aware of the components of the payload (scientific instrumentation) because they have checked them out for compatibility with their own radio and telemetry equipment. In such cases there is particular interest and affection for the neophyte space neighbor. As it zooms upward into space they remember its unique assortment of information-gathering devices; its television cameras, its meters to measure radiation and micrometeorites. They remember that it is operating on solar batteries or other power sources, and that its instruments will take weather pictures and make measurements of the strange world beyond our earthly atmosphere.

The data these satellites collect will be transmitted to earth via radio signals. And even as the radio trackers are reducing the "beep-beep" signals of the talking instruments, so are the optical trackers observing the satellite's location in space because changes in the orbit indicate the effects of solar pressure, gravity drag and other phenomena. Such observations have told us much about the size and shape of the earth and of gravitational fields and have even resulted in changes in the world maps we read today.

Outwardly, our sky rangers, who ride herd on the growing list of satellites, seem calm, nerveless, and businesslike. This is because they dare not fly off the handle and make a wrong decision. Few men in the world today have such awesome responsibilities for life, property, and the advancement of science as do our trackers. And so, as the great bird moves from the pad at the launch center, the symphony of satellite networks around the world begins to perform. Sometimes

Military men need to keep track of everything that is going on in space so that they can provide warning and protection should an attack from space occur. Shown here is the huge radar antenna at Thule, Greenland, a member of the Ballistic Missiles Early Warning System (BMEWS).

the sky rangers are like maestros sitting at giant consoles, manipulating masses of switches, knobs, and dials, as flashing red and green lights dance on their control boards. Other times they are tense military men huddled around the digital computers which have just informed them that another Soviet satellite is orbiting over the North American Continent. Is it friendly? Is it spying? Has it a hostile purpose?

Questions, questions, questions.

Our civilian scientific people need to know the answers to the mysteries they send satellites out to investigate. Military men need to keep track of everything that is going on in space so that they can provide warning and protection should an attack from space occur. The entire scientific and military community of the free world needs to know what is going on in space; and only the symphony of satellite tracking networks can tell them.

Stations around the world keep tabs on the satellite's innermost secrets. Should it explode, even its fragments are carefully observed and documented—orbit after orbit. Old-timers and new-timers, gregarious "beepers" and stolid "silent" types, and just plain junk have assigned addresses in space. Satellite tracking is big business these days. In cost, it amounts to billions of dollars. In national prestige, it has helped close the mortifying gap in space technology between the United States and Russia. Whatever benefits we hope to derive from space exploration in the future will depend largely upon the skill and dedication of our sky rangers.

In many ways, satellite tracking is a strange profession. We wonder about the call that drives men into the remotest, most Godforsaken places on our globe so that they may serve as the eyes and ears of the space age. What possible satisfaction do they get as they struggle with primitive housing, severe weather, loneliness, rattlesnakes, mosquitoes, black bears, kangaroos, red tape, boredom, hostile tribesmen, and even revolutions? These problems, all seemingly unrelated, are typical companions to groups of men in far-flung tracking stations. Some stations are located within driving distances of exotic modern cities, but they are rare. The very nature of the trackers' business demands that they be remote from the radio and sky-light interference of a metropolis. To put it bluntly, the trackers' personal comfort is the very last consideration when station sites are chosen.

Why then do they choose this profession?

The answer most often given is that space technology is new and they want to be in on it; they want to do something that no one has done before. Pioneers? Of course they are, in every sense of the word. In the early days of tracking, some men selected for overseas stations fitted a cartoonist's dream of the eccentric, the "nut," the bearded individualist.

As tracking became more streamlined and "settled" the eccentrics gave way to the businesslike family man, so that no longer can we pick someone out of the crowd and say "Aha, there's a tracker." However, today's sky ranger is not dull; his job is a constant challenge. He knows what he is doing now, but he is constantly learning. There is newer, more complicated, more highly sensitive equipment with which to work and his "herd" of satellites has grown from one little Sputnik in October 1957 to more than five hundred in the skies today.

It has been a long hard struggle for trackers to attain their present capability of knowing where everything is in space, of being able to command, guide, and converse with the man-made moons and deep probes that are hundreds of thousands of miles away. But even with today's sophisticated systems, sky rangers are far from satisfied. "Space tracking is in its infancy," they say. "We have just begun to crawl."

If it is an infant now, perhaps we should look back to the days when the satellite tracking profession was born.

2

Sputnik and the IGY

"BEEP . . . Beep . . . Beep . . ."

The signals were weak and came from five hundred-sixty miles out. Aesthetically, they left much to be desired, but that day they were number one on the world's hit parade. There had never been anything like it in the history of mankind. "Sounds like a cricket with a sore throat," someone at NBC suggested. "Or a frog trying to sing Calypso . . ." The signals were three-tenths of a second long, with a pause of the same length.

It was October 4, 1957 that Russia successfully launched Sputnik I, the world's first artificial satellite. The 185-pound ball had been shot upward at about five miles per second, reaching five hundred-sixty miles at apogee (farthest point from earth), and one hundred-seventy miles at perigee (closest point to earth), in its elliptical looping around the globe.

For the Communist propagandists, the feat was a smash victory. Their announcement boasted, "The successful launching of the first man-made satellite makes a tremendous contribution to the treasure house of world science and culture. Artificial earth satellites will pave the way for space travel, and it seems that the present generation will witness how the freed and conscious labor of the people of the new socialist society turns even the most daring of man's dreams into reality. . . ."

The scientific community around the world shared the Russians' jubilation. For them, a great door had been opened and mankind had gone through. Now the door was forever closed behind and there would be no way to go but up—and out into the vast sea of space. Astronomers would no longer be considered a luxury class of useless, impractical thinkers. Once more, those who studied the heavens would, like Newton, Galileo, and Kepler, lead mankind to adventures in new worlds.

The shock effects of Sputnik were varied and intriguing, considering that only a few short years ago outer space was still in the realm of scientists, Buck Rogers, and Flash Gordon. Young people took the event in their stride. Children loved it and could not understand the concern and bewilderment of their parents. Toy manufacturers brought out space suits, ray guns and T-shirts with satellites appliqued on the front. Telescopes and binoculars were no longer advertised as tools for bird watching but became "satellite-tracking" instruments. Do-it-yourself kits, complete with astronomical maps for home satellite-tracking stations were found in most corner drugstores. Sales conferences featured pretty girls popping out of balloon gondolas.

To thousands of Americans, the feat that shook the earth had badly shaken their sense of security. They felt a strange mixture of awe, admiration, and fear at the realization that a Russian satellite was passing overhead some four to six times a day. Actually there were three satellites—

Sputnik itself, a section of the launching rocket, and its nose cone. For those who followed the Bible in a literal way, there were religious implications which were difficult to resolve. Such people always thought that things in the sky were put there by God—yet here was something brand-new in the skies which although it wasn't put there by God, must have been put there by somebody awfully close to Him.

The clamor of the public for information was fantastic. Sightings of all sorts of mysterious objects were reported by phone, mail, and telegram. The press, totally unprepared for highly technical space-science reporting, used a variety of political, crime, and straight news reporters to cover Sputnik's journey. Misquotes were the rule; sensationalism rampant. At the Smithsonian Astrophysical Observatory (of which we shall hear more later) the ladies' lounge became the "Astrophysical Press Association," literally a classroom for scientists to explain to the press just what was going on. *Life* magazine wanted to know where to send an airplane in order to photograph Sputnik. "Cost is no object!" Said Dr. J. Allen Hynek of Smithsonian Astrophysical Observatory (SAO), "If I had said Tierra del Fuego, within minutes, the *Life* crew would have been dispatched there. . . ."

To have the Russians beat us with that first space shot was a real jolt to the complacency—the ego—of the American people. To step to the foot of the class at a time when we were grabbing for prestige in the eyes of newly formed independent countries and tottering older governments seemed intolerable, especially in the light of our soaring taxes.

Why couldn't we have launched ours in time to grab the spotlight? *What* and *who* were responsible?

Comments came from all quarters. Interservice rivalry among the military was blamed. Budget problems entered into the controversy. Scientists felt that the reason for delay of our satellite launch was the American people's attitude toward science and scientists. They pointed out that while we were treating our patriotic scientists with hostility and suspicion, Russia was building a scientific elite. They urged more aid and encouragement to our educational institutions in turning out more engineers and scientists, especially at the graduate level.

But even as we lost the first round of the race, some historians found a silver lining. Alfred Rosenthal, historian at Goddard Space Flight Center states in the official publication, *The Early Years*, "The people engaged in existing satellite programs had a difficult time explaining that their best efforts had been hampered by limitations over which they had no control. However, the end results of the new 'space consciousness' were very beneficial, since there developed a general realization that the American effort had to be greatly expanded and financially supported. . . ."

We were indeed space conscious and many people who had paid little attention to such terms as "International Geophysical Year (IGY)" and "Project Vanguard" now took a good hard look at them. What did they mean? What was going on, anyway?

The IGY, they learned, was not a year at all, but eighteen months, extending from July 1, 1957, to December 31, 1958. Its goal was to expand knowledge of the earth, its gaseous mantle known as the atmosphere, and the adjacent region of space beyond the bulk of the atmosphere. Generally referred to as "the most successful cooperative enterprise ever undertaken by man," the IGY involved thousands of scientists from sixty-seven nations, all dedicated to the pursuit of knowledge about our physical environment.

Once the idea for an IGY was agreed upon, each country organized its national committee. The chairman for the United States committee was Dr. Joseph Kaplan, Professor of Physics at the University of California at Los Angeles. In October of 1954, the United States first really considered launching an instrumented satellite as phase #1 of the program. A study group, called the LPR (Long Playing Rocket) was formed under the direction of Dr. Fred Whipple, and its task was to report on the geophysical possibilities, technical feasibility, budget controls, manpower, timing, cost estimates, desired orbit, and so on.

The LPR committee came up with the suggestion that the United States should indeed put a satellite into orbit for peaceful scientific-research purposes. They further suggested that it be twenty inches in diameter and painted white so as to be visually observed from the ground with binoculars on specialized cameras. Even in those preliminary planning stages, scientists knew how useless the satellite would be if it could not be properly tracked.

The committee concluded that with the proper funds and manpower a satellite for payloads of ten pounds could be made within two or three years. On March 10, 1955, the United States committee adopted a resolution favoring the launching of instrumented satellites. July 29, 1955, the White House announced to the world that the United States would launch small unmanned, earth-circling satellites as a part of the United States participation in the IGY. We would call our project "Vanguard" meaning first, or forefront.

3

Project Vanguard and the Development of Minitrack

ONCE it was decided that the United States would toss its IGY hat into the ring—or space, as it were—with an orbiting scientific satellite, the Vanguard project was then sliced into three main parts:

1. The National Academy of Sciences was to determine the experiments to be orbited.

2. The National Science Foundation was to supply the necessary funds.

3. The Department of Defense (DOD) would launch the satellite.

Several proposals were considered within DOD, and finally the decision was made to go ahead with the Navy's proposal to launch a satellite, using the Viking, a multistage rocket built by the Martin Company of Baltimore, Maryland. The Martin field crew would be largely responsible for the launchings, while Naval Research Laboratory (NRL) personnel and other Naval officers would provide a sort of over-all technical monitoring. The Viking was to be the first stage;

the Aerobee the second. The third, a solid fuel rocket of five hundred pounds of thrust was yet to be developed. On top would be placed a nose cone weighing twenty pounds. This included the scientific experiment to be orbited.

Briefly, the Navy program's goals were to (a) develop and procure a satellite-launching vehicle, (b) place at least one satellite in orbit during the IGY, (c) accomplish at least one scientific experiment with the satellite, and (d) track the satellite's flight, to demonstrate that it had actually orbited.

When you remember that everything was new, the tasks facing the Vanguard people were fantastic—all theory and inference. There was no experience to use as guidelines, no textbooks for reference; these men were writing such textbooks with their day-to-day work.

They knew of course that in order for the satellite to stay in orbit its velocity must be five miles per second. It was figured that the satellite would be in a slightly elliptical orbit, no closer than two hundred miles from the earth's surface at perigee (closest point) and no farther than fifteen hundred miles at apogee (farthest point). The orbit would be at a forty-degree angle to the equator in the zone between the fortieth latitudes north and south. With an orbital velocity of 18,000 miles per hour, the satellite would circle the earth in about one hundred minutes, or fourteen to sixteen times a day.

The vehicle would be self-guided by a control system built into the second rocket. This control system would time the ignition and separation of the spent rockets, and would direct the jets of the gimbal-mounted motors of the first and second stage to swing the vehicle smoothly from its vertical trajectory to a course parallel to the earth's surface. Just before the control system ignited the third stage it would fire a pinwheel array of jets. The third stage, spinning at several revolutions per second, would streak away in stable flight on the orbit. Hopefully.

So far, so good. But where do you shoot the bird from?

Scientists knew that the satellite would have to be launched in an easterly direction in order to take advantage of the earth's rotational velocity of 1,300 feet per second (1,000 miles per hour) and give it a kind of slingshot effect. This ruled out White Sands, New Mexico, where the Viking facilities were already set up; there was danger of the last stage falling on populated areas.

Roosevelt Roads in Puerto Rico was considered, but ruled out because of the expense. What about Cape Canaveral (now Kennedy)? But, said the Vanguard people, this area was built to launch ballistic missiles which did not require the precise measurements of Vanguard. Also downrange facilities would be needed, because Vanguard, unlike the Army's ballistic missile, was multistage, requiring command and control points as far away as 1,000 miles. Still, the Cape was the best from the location and weather points of view.

There was no way out of the dilemma except for the Navy to move their facilities from White Sands to the Cape. They would have to build their own blockhouse, launch pad, gantries—the works; also, they must construct their own downrange facilities. The Navy's Vanguard group quite literally constructed the United States' first complete satellite-launch facility almost from the ground up.

What was it like in those days when a whole new breed of men was preparing to shoot for the unknown regions of space? Today's space experts shake their heads in wonder that things went as well as they did—considering the obstacles. "Those were the days," they say. The days of a Foreign Legion atmosphere, mosquitoes, rattlesnakes, tired greasy hamburgers and coffee from the Pan American lunch truck, affectionately called the Roach Coach. They were the

Those were the days when a whole new breed of men worked long hours in the muggy heat or bitter cold of a south Florida swampland—known today as Cape Kennedy. Shown here is a Vanguard shot, primitive by today's standards, but an enormous effort for its time.

long hours of work in the muggy heat or bitter cold of a south Florida swampland; of fumbling, groping, sweating, and praying each time a countdown rolled around. Our Vanguard people could tell by the way the bird looked and sounded just how the show would go because they were almost looking up its tailpipe. There was a ditch nearby, usually full of snakes, and it was often suggested that it might be a battle for that ditch between men and snakes should the men have to make a dive for it.

They were the days of too much publicity for untried tests, for sudden and even embarrassing interest from an administration which had previously thought little of space efforts. Prior to Sputnik, Secretary of Defense Charles E. Wilson thought it was all "stuff and nonsense." He said, "Research is when you don't know what you're doing."

Dr. Paul Walsh, Deputy Director on the project, recalls visits of Washington VIP's. "Secretary of the Navy Gates was all for it of course. I remember one day he patted me on the back and said, 'Son, I don't know what in hell you're doing down here, but good luck.'"

It was a time for the mild-mannered, pipe-smoking astrophysicist Dr. John P. Hagen who headed Project Vanguard, to keep tempers and emotions from exploding by simply remaining calm himself. "We'll try again," he'd say as he toted his lunch to work every day in a little black lunch box. His working day was often sixteen hours.

It was a time when the White House was literally scheduling shots—ready or not. Vanguard people say those schedules were murder.

It was a time too for men who would become sky rangers to plunge in on the job of creating systems for tracking satellites that had not yet been built, let alone shot into orbit. They didn't know how much time they had but they vowed they'd have as much of an organizational headstart on the orbiting satellite as possible. And in the beginning, they didn't even know *what* they would be required to track. The Vanguard people had been planning on a simple nose cone. Then, the National Academy of Sciences announced that it wanted a satellite which was spherical in shape, about thirty inches in diameter.

Even as the Vanguard people paled and shook their heads in protest, the scientists insisted, "We need a spherical shape in order to carry out the experiments."

The Vanguard people scratched their heads and pondered the problem. "How about compromising with a twenty-inch sphere?"

"Agreed."

By March of 1956, the Vanguard had been redesigned. Six test vehicles and seven satellite-launching vehicles were scheduled for production. The Martin Company built the first stage, Aerojet Corporation the second, and Grand Central Rocket Company and Allegheny Ballistics Laboratory were developing the third stage.

On December 8, 1956, TV-0 (test vehicle) which was actually Viking 13 modified for this shot, reached an altitude of 126 miles. TV-1, in May of 1957, ignited, separated successfully and flew 450 miles farther than TV-0's 183 miles. There was great jubilation because the solid fuel upper stage had been ignited during flight. In July, 1957, the Naval Research Laboratory (NRL) directed that the instrument test packages be changed to small six-inch satellite spheres.

By October 23, 1957, the first complete Vanguard configuration or complete package along with flight test of the first stage engine was performed, and on December 6, 1957, the now famous TV-3 shot was scheduled. Workers at the Cape were soon in for a big surprise. It seems the White House decided that this would be the shot that would put a satellite into orbit. According to announcements, TV-3 would be America's answer to Sputnik!

But, protested the Vanguard people, this is a *test*; this is the first time it has been flown in all three stages. Sure, the bird had been tested at the plant, there had been static firing and it had been checked in every possible way. "But," Paul Walsh explains, "there comes a time when the only way to really find out is to fly it. When that happens, there is no turning back."

The whole world, it seemed, was watching. Hundreds of pressmen waited with poised pencils. Crowds of tourists . . . President Eisenhower . . . everybody. *Life* magazine's photographers aimed their cameras as the countdown neared zero.

Kurt Stehling, a senior engineer on the project, describes in his book *"Project Vanguard"* just what that heartbreaking moment was like:

T-0 seconds. The final fire switch was closed. The last second-stage umbilical cord dropped. The rocket engine began to show sparks and fire as the pyrotechnic igniter in its inside ignited the beginning of the oxygen and kerosene fumes. The time was 11:44.559 A.M. America's first satellite was about to take off.

The engine started with a heartrending, hoarse, whining moan like that of some antediluvian beast in birth pain. Flame filled the nozzle, dispiritedly at first and then built up with a great crescendo to a tremendous howl, brilliantly white, streaked with black. The vehicle shook itself momentarily like a wet dog. Ice and snow fell off the sides. The banshee howl of the engine increased. The vehicle hesitatingly ripped itself loose from its iron womb and rose slowly. We rose up with it on our tiptoes.

"Look out! Oh, God, no!" somebody screamed.

It seemed as if all the gates of Hell had opened up. Brilliant stiletto flames shot out from the side of the rocket near the engine. The vehicle agonizingly hesitated a moment, quivered again and, in front of our unbelieving, shocked eyes, began to topple. It also sank like a great flaming sword into its scabbard down into the blast tube. It toppled slowly, breaking apart, hitting part of the test stand and ground with a tremendous roar that could be felt and heard even behind the two-foot concrete walls of the blockhouse and the six-inch-thick bulletproof glass. For a moment or two there was complete disbelief. I could see it in the faces, I could feel it myself. This just couldn't be.

An immense cloud of red flame from burning propellants engulfed the whole area. Someone shouted "Duck" and by reaction alone almost everybody ducked down. I was frozen still: I couldn't. My back began to hurt with the same nervous ache I had one time when I was in an aircraft whose engine was on fire. The fire control technician madly pulled the water-deluge lever and thousands of gallons of water sprayed into the steaming smoking inferno. We now crowded to the windows. The fire died down and we saw America's supposed response to the 200-pound Sputnik satellite—our 4-pound "grapefruit"—lying amid the scattered glowing debris and, unbelievably, still beeping away, unharmed. C619300 ⚙ SCHOOLS

But in that instant of pain and despair, every ashen face in our control room showed a common resolution echoed by Mazur—"O.K., let's clean up: let's get the next rocket ready."

TV-3 was dead. A vast outcry of derision and anguish frothed up abroad and in the United States. Mighty America's prestige, seemingly dependent on a small 72-foot rocket, was collapsing!

The center spread in *Life* magazine was a picture of Vanguard—on fire. There was no mention of the fact that the shot itself was pure bonus—a research-type test. Not even a hint was made that perhaps the Soviets had had similar disasters. The *Manchester Guardian* was one of the rare publications that saw the picture in its proper perspective. Their article, entitled "The Story that Got Out of Hand," was clipped, framed, and hung on the walls of Vanguard offices in gratitude that at least *somebody* understood.

The word *Vanguard* had a kind of bitter, ironic ring to it, following Sputnik and Mutnik, but there was still hope that it could be the first American satellite to orbit. Even this hope was dashed when the Army orbited Explorer I, on January 31, 1958. Explorer I was responsible for the discovery of the Van Allen radiation belt—believed to be the most significant finding of the IGY. It demonstrated the feasibility of temperature control by satellite surface treatment and showed that micrometeorites are not necessarily a major consideration in space travel near the earth.

But Vanguard was our IGY project and Vanguard would prove its worth. On the 17th of March, 1958, TV-4 successfully launched Vanguard I, a 6-inch sphere weighing only four pounds. Although it was far from the 20-inch sphere the United States had planned to orbit in the beginning, it did confirm the merit of the Vanguard rocket design. Three other Vanguard rocket launches were made before the team of about a hundred men transferred to the newly created civilian agency, National Aeronautics and Space Administration (NASA).

In retrospect, it is interesting to look back on that frantic era. Considering the failures and delays, was it worth it? Says Admiral Rossen Bennett, who was Chief of Naval Research during the IGY, "Remember that Project Vanguard was run on a shoestring in comparison with such magnificently funded space projects as Pioneer and Discoverer. The public got its money's worth, particularly in view of the fact that much of Vanguard was transferred to NASA as a complete package."

Dr. Kaplan, mentioned earlier as former chairman of the American committee of the IGY, states that ". . . Project Vanguard gave us a real start, and in terms of scientific accomplishments of the past few years and the promise of the future, it was a magnificent start. . . ."

Interestingly enough, that little "grapefruit" as Khruschev called it, kept beeping away for more than six years, and will continue to orbit for at least 2,000 years. Scientists took a second look at the tiny fellow which was launched during a period of maximum solar activity. We are now in a period of quiet sun activity. Vanguard was the only satellite in orbit which could give us information to contrast the two periods.

One of the most valuable contributions of Project Vanguard and one which is still in use, is the "Minitrack" system of tracking satellites. This was the fourth requirement set up during the IGY: to track a satellite's flight to demonstrate that it had actually orbited.

Track a satellite?

Obviously there was no point in putting a satellite into orbit unless it could feed its information back to its earthly masters. A system of tracking would have to be developed before any space shot was made. First requirement was to find the thing, once we got it up there. It would be like looking for a needle in a haystack as the satellite whirled through outer space at 18,000 miles per hour. It would be comparable to trying to find a golf ball dropped from a jet plane flying at the speed of sound at 60,000 feet. To further complicate matters, the satellite would disappear from view when it went around to the opposite side of the globe and each time it reappeared would have to be found again.

Two hundred miles is a long way up. During the day, the sun would outshine the dim point of light, the man-made moon. At night it could not be seen unless it were artificially illuminated (there were no such plans for Vanguard). Visually, when the sun was below the horizon, the light of the sky would be reduced while the satellite shone clear and bright, fully illuminated by the sun. It would be like a twinkling star against a black background.

A good-sized problem, all right. Too bad there wasn't a

textbook to refer to, or some genius who could quickly produce the tricky formula for success. In lieu of these, rationalization, skilled engineering and some Yankee ingenuity would have to suffice.

Thinking the problem out, the experts realized that a satellite could be *seen*, but as has been said, only at twilight and dawn when the sky is free of blanketing clouds. This could be a job for the optical trackers (of whom we shall hear later).

But a satellite could also be *heard* if it were equipped with transmitting equipment and if there were receivers on earth to listen.

The men sat down and began figuring. Point number one was, what do we have in existence that might be modified to suit our present needs? Roger Easton of NRL, recalls how the Vanguard trackers simply "snitched" the system from Azusa, Convair's method for guiding the Atlas. "It only took us about fifteen minutes to modify the guidance system used for the Atlas to a satellite tracking system for Vanguard." The modification is called "Minitrack," a name dreamed up by John T. Mengel, who is now with NASA. It stands for *minimum-weight tracking system*, and utilizes a "radio interferometer" technique.

The best way of illustrating how it works is by comparing it to an animal's two ears which would be pointed in the direction of a sound. These "ears" or antennae pick up the radio signal from the satellite, and the exact measurement of the signal's angular direction gives the orbital data from which the satellite can be tracked. The antennae on the ground project fan-shaped beams, with widths of several hundred miles at orbiting heights.

In addition to being comparatively simple, Minitrack has many advantages. For one thing, it does not need an acquisition aid (no previous help before it picks up a signal) such as radar, and it can operate around the clock, day or night, rain or shine, as opposed to optical tracking. It picks up a satellite's signal on each pass.

The original Minitrack stations of the IGY era were comparatively simple affairs. They generally consisted of an 80- by 20-foot headquarters building to be used for operational purposes, concrete pads for truck-mounted electronic equipment, a guard building, and nine precisely located antennae which covered several acres. A basic interferometer (an instrument used for measuring wave lengths) was arranged like a cross, with a separation between antennae of about five hundred feet. For timing synchronization, each station had a receiver to pick up signals from WWV, the National Bureau of Standards Station that sends out a beat every second, accurate to one hundred-millionth of a second.

Minitrack radio receivors were to be sensitive to signals of 108 megacycles during the IGY. It is interesting to note that the Russians did catch us with our antennae down because Sputnik I broadcast on a frequency of 20 to 40 megacycles instead of the agreed-upon 108 megacycles. There had been an article in the Soviet magazine *Radio* which announced the change in frequencies, but it was several weeks before the article was translated into English. When news of Sputnik, along with the announcement of the new frequency reached the United States, no less than thirty NRL personnel scrambled to change their frequency in order to track Sputnik. Hal Hoff of NRL, one of the men who worked all night long, made a recording of Sputnik's signals, and played it at an IGY symposium so that the Russians could hear it for the first time.

Of course one station would do very little good in tracking objects of varying orbits and inclinations. There would have to be a number of them, forming a kind of fence along the

75th meridian, which would reach from Washington, D.C. to Santiago, Chile. Every satellite in an equatorial orbit would have to cross this fence at one point or another.

But where would these stations be set up?

Colonel Robert C. Miller, who was appointed Chief of Project Vanguard Task Force, U.S. Army Map Service, along with Captain Win Berg, USN, and others, set out on a site-finding trip along their north-south fence. What under usual circumstances could have been a ticklish diplomatic dilemma turned out to be a heartening experience in inter-American cooperation. Colonel Miller was an ideal choice for this assignment. Having been Director of the Inter-American Geodetic Survey group for five and a half years he knew those countries and cultures south of the border. Captain Berg is a master at getting along with people, as we shall later see.

The sites chosen were Blossom Point, Maryland; Fort Stewart, Georgia; Quito, Ecuador; Lima, Peru; Antofagasta, Chile; Santiago, Chile; San Diego, California; Woomera, Australia; Olifantsfontein, Republic of South Africa; Antigua, West Indies; and Havana, Cuba. On the latter station, Captain Berg recalls, "Castro was stirring up trouble at the time so we had a reversible sign. One side said 'Batista Field,' and the other side said 'Castro Field.'"

The construction of the stations, which was the job of the U.S. Army Engineers, resembled in many ways the building of Vanguard itself. Everything had to be built from the ground up, under the most primitive of conditions. Sites which had been nothing but pinpoints on the map had to be cleared. Roads had to be built, communications set up, equipment had to be shipped and then hauled up winding mountain roads to the sites. Often erection crews were halfway through a job when they found they were missing vital parts. Even after they cabled their requirements, there would be errors in shipment. The Engineers finally got to the point of marking all their shipments with a big red "VANGUARD" stamp and Pan American hurried them through.

During the IGY, the Army had the responsibility of manning the stations. In all, ninety-eight enlisted technicians, seventeen civilian experts and six officers were drawn from the Army Engineer and Signal Corps. All had been trained in Army schools and at NRL. After the IGY, Bendix Field Engineering personnel (Bendix did the actual construction of the Minitrack equipment) under contract to NASA, took over responsibility of the stations. Today, stations in most foreign countries are manned by local indigenous personnel trained in the United States by NASA and Bendix Field Engineering personnel.

Choosing sites, training personnel, building and manning of stations were only part of the problems of the early sky rangers. Since a satellite had not yet been launched, how did anyone know the system would work? The Army came up with the suggestion that as their technicians had been bouncing signals off the moon since 1946, they could build a transmitter which would operate on Minitrack's 108 megacycles. They could operate it with a 60-foot antenna, send signals to the moon, and bounce them back to the various Minitrack stations. This method proved very useful for calibration purposes and for locating various flaws in the system.

Another major problem was that of setting up communications between each Minitrack station and the Vanguard Control Center at NRL as quickly as possible. From NRL, the orbital data would flow immediately to the Vanguard Computing Center in Washington, D.C. where the International Business Machines Corporation (IBM) 704 computer would determine and predict the orbits. Computer programmers and mathematicians had issued about 40,000 instructions to the remarkable machine so that it could immediately produce workable data. The computer's orbital predictions would then be flashed to all stations so that they would be ready for the next "pass."

The tremendous job of setting up these communications was taken over by the Army's Signal Corps. In addition to individual teletype circuits to each station, there were to be sixteen commercial lines connecting the stations with the United States. It was a rugged, back-breaking job considering the far-flung areas that simply had to be tied together. At last the job was done. The Minitrack stations were ready for America's shot into space.

Today, communication all around the world is fantastically swift. Information is received on a satellite's behavior in "real time," as it happens. Giant 709 computers spew out reams of workable data in split seconds. But only a few short years ago, men were bent over graphs and plotting boards, doing everything by hand. Martin Votaw recalls those days at the Cape. "We were in Hangar S during the launches. It was an air-conditioned room where we ran tests on payloads before launches . . . measuring frequencies and so on. After the satellite was on the rocket and bolted down we'd run back to the room and use the electronic equipment to see what was going on. We worked out a kind of Doppler plot (measuring the change in the wavelength between the source and the observer. Similar to the sound of a passing train whistle . . . *eeeoong*). One fellow did the Doppler readings while the other fellow jotted on a graph paper. Actually, Doppler is used on all launches now, but it started out as a general interest thing so the guys working on the payload would know what was going on."

Martin Votaw, who was with Vanguard, did admit to a bit of friendly rivalry with the Army. "Dr. George Ludwig

Project Vanguard was completed September 18, 1959. A series of fourteen were tested at Cape Kennedy. Seven were launches designed to place a scientific earth satellite into orbit as part of the United States contribution to the IGY. Other vehicles were fired as test units without upper stages.

was the scientific experimenter with the Army's Explorer I through V. His equipment provided the measurements for the discovery of the Van Allen belt. Well, the Army had two huts, very small, six-foot cube. One had tracking gear in it, the other had telemetry. When it came time for the shots, poor Dr. Ludwig, who is six feet tall, had to come to our nose-cone room where we had the Doppler set up in order to get his telemetry read out, because there was no room for him in the Army huts.

"Of course we'd have been in there plotting the course whether Ludwig was there or not. We wanted to see if they'd made it or not." Votaw, who was then in his early thirties, and who even now looks the part of the puckish young genius, recalls further, "I remember on Explorer II the 4th stage didn't light. By our calculations, the curve on our plot went down two steps and then coasted. After the launch the Army announced that it was successful. 'Oh, no,' we said. Twenty-four hours later the Army had to rescind the statement.

"We started asking the Army if they'd like to see our Doppler plot. They'd say, 'Yeah, bring it over.'

"On Explorer V, we asked, 'Wanna see our Doppler plot?' 'Yeah, bring it over.'

"So I took it over. The door opened a crack and a hand reached out and grabbed the paper. Then the door was slammed shut. They didn't even let me in."

Such memories make for great reminiscing sessions for the Project Vanguard people and our early sky rangers. Each year a party for Vanguard alumni is held at the Goddard Space Flight Center, Greenbelt, Maryland. Scientists, technicians, engineers, and rocketmen, who have scattered to the four winds in other space projects, return to toast the good old crazy and frantic days of the IGY. Prominently displayed in a place of honor is a little brightly polished mock-up of a satellite named *Vanguard*.

4

Minitrack Today

WITH the close of the IGY and the establishment of the National Aeronautics and Space Administration (NASA), many of the original Minitrack stations transferred over to the civilian agency as a complete package. Responsibility for them was assigned to the Goddard Space Flight Center (GSFC) in Greenbelt, Maryland, which in turn contracted Bendix Field Engineering to provide operation and maintenance.

The original Minitrack equipment was supplemented by additional tracking and telemetry equipment. Now a part of Goddard's satellite tracking and data acquisition network (STADAN), the stations have the additional responsibility for data gathering. One important change was the conversion from 108 megacycles which was allowed by the Federal Communications Commission during the IGY to the more efficient 136 megacycles. This higher frequency gives much greater accuracy of angular measurement. Minitrack's worldwide timing error is only two to four milliseconds (thousandths of a second) absolute.

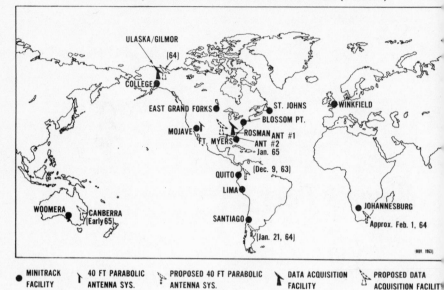

Much of the credit for Minitrack's accuracy can be given to the satellite network's two DC-4 airplanes whose job it is to fly over the stations as a simulated satellite in order to calibrate equipment on the ground with theirs in the planes. Affectionately called "Cal planes," these heavily instrumented aircraft fly to every remote STADAN station in the world, averaging 200,000 miles each year. In many ways, their crews find themselves in one of the world's strangest flying jobs because they must be not only excellent airplane pilots but highly skilled technicians as well. To fly safely over vast distances is only one part of the job. Crews must schedule their appearances over the Minitrack station during good "calibration weather," that is, when stars can be photographed. The photographs of the stars are then used as a basic reference for the radio system field evaluation.

Just what is good calibration weather?

A slight haze is not good. A clear night with a bright moon may be prohibitive, as well, because the stars will not show up distinctly. Rain and storms, of course, rule out a successful "flyby." Ideal weather then is a calm, clear, not-too-bright night.

Cal plane crews learn to "play for the spots"—the clearings in the sky—regardless of temperature. Some stations provide

Minitrack Station in Winkfield, England, calibrates its own ground equipment. Shown here is the calibration camera used for this purpose.

the crew with peculiar circumstances that make calibration more difficult. For example, the Quito, Ecuador, site sits under a small friendly cloud a half-mile square about seventy percent of the time. This is due to the high altitude of the station—about 11,700 feet—and a nearby mountain. It is up to the Cal plane to check in on Quito during the thirty percent good weather. Since calibration of Minitrack stations must be done twice a year, Quito is visited in November and May.

For Alaska, September and March have proved to be the best times. This is because of the long daylight hours during the intervening period.

Sites at Woomera, Johannesburg, and Winkfield, England, are not evaluated by the STADAN network plane; their calibration is the responsibility ·of the countries in which they are operated.

So efficient is the system that Cal planes have taken on calibration of additional tracking and telemetry equipment and numerous special tests necessary in the development and acceptance of stations other than Minitrack. Included in the new assignments are flyover tests of radar "dish" antenna sites, range and range-rate and laser optical tracking systems (all of which we shall explore later).

Cal planes and new equipment have updated Minitrack stations considerably since the IGY. New locations have also widened their capabilities. Facilities at Fort Stewart, Georgia, have been moved to Fort Myer, Florida. Stations at Antigua, B.W.I., and Havana, Cuba, have been discontinued. The San Diego, California, station has been moved to Goldstone, California. Both Fort Stewart and San Diego are prominent in the military tracking picture as we shall later see. There are four new stations in the NASA Minitrack network: St. Johns, Newfoundland; East Grand Forks, Minnesota; Fairbanks, Alaska; and Winkfield, England. The last four have been established to track satellites which have been put into a polar orbit. The station at Santiago, Chile has been discontinued and plans are now under way to close the first Minitrack station ever to be established—Blossom Point, Maryland, near Washington, D.C.

It seems sad in a way, as if an era were drawing to a close, but sky rangers must never allow sentiment to interfere with progress. Satellites are not what they used to be— simple, transmitting, low-inclination (its orbital plane inclined to the equator) packages. Now, we have satellites that look for all the world like enormous, brightly colored insects with antennae and paddles sticking out all over. "Hatboxes" and gigantic balloons are whirling through space while a tidy package known as Syncom remains tethered in a parking orbit. Where once we worried about putting up a tiny satellite weighing just a few pounds, we are now involved in putting up packages of three thousand pounds. The days of the nice, tidy low inclination orbit have given way to highly elliptical patterns that reach far outside Minitrack's "earshot." Only the "big dish" radars can reach out far enough with their electronic arms to monitor and keep a check on deep space probes. Minitrack must give way to more sophisticated newcomers, even as it continues to do its yeoman chores, 365 days a year, 24 hours each day.

What would it be like to be a sky ranger at, say, the Blossom Point Tracking station? One way of finding out is to pay a visit.

The first thing you notice is the striking contrast between the rural Maryland countryside and the steel-gray, air-conditioned prefab buildings at the station. It is as if yesterday and tomorrow stood there, side by side, and this feeling seems to hold true for most tracking stations around the world. At Blossom Point, expert technicians are tracking and collecting data from satellites that are hundreds of miles

The first station to be built in the Minitrack system during the IGY was at Blossom Point, Maryland. The reservation consists of about twenty acres of forest out of which has been hacked a clearing for the buildings and tracking gear. To the left of the operations building can be seen an experimental 16-element Yagi antenna. The flat antennae are the conventional Minitrack.

in space, while their neighbors down the road are milking fat cows, churning butter, and hoeing the garden, much as they did in their grandparents' days. Even the language is different, for sky rangers discuss read-outs, orbital inclinations, taking a pass, telemeters, using a whole new vocabulary built around initials. STADAN, SPADATS, SAO, NAVSPASUR, and so on, all mean something to trackers, but confront the folks at the local country store with such mystifying tongue-twisters and the coverall-clad shoulders shrug in bewilderment.

The reservation itself consists of about twenty acres of beautiful forest out of which has been hacked a clearing for the buildings and tracking gear. Located near La Plata, Maryland, an area rich in history (historical markers point out such interest spots as the home site of the Surgeon General of the Revolutionary Army) we find other towns consisting merely of a store and a gas pump: Port Tobacco, Welcome, and McKonchie. If you are lucky you will find the place where you turn off the main highway and plunge up the narrow dirt road past barns and old houses and contented cattle grazing in the meadows. A visitor can easily get lost, for there are no signs to point the way.

At last you see evidence of "tomorrow" in the form of barbed wire fencing with red, white, and blue NASA insignia and "U.S. Government Property. Keep Out." Fortunately the welcome mat is out for those who have suitable authorization. The buildings in the center of the clearing are intensely quiet. Trucks and cars are parked and silent. Minitrack antennae spread out in the field seem to say, "Shhhhh. We're listening."

At the edge of the clearing a beautiful doe nibbles unconcernedly on a choice bush. As many as twenty deer may turn up for a daily visit. Fox, beaver, wild rabbit, and other game live in the quiet sanctuary, content that Uncle Sam will protect them from hunters.

Inside the main building (which is divided in half, with telemetry equipment forward and Minitrack gear in the back) we see some of the sky rangers in action. There is a shirt-sleeved man watching a teletype message coming through on wide yellow paper. Around the corner another man with headsets perches on a stool in front of ceiling-high instruments. He fiddles with knobs and dials; he is getting ready to take the next Echo pass. A few feet away, a sky ranger is down on his hands and knees with a long ream of graph paper on which jiggly lines have been etched. He frowns, makes notations, and seems to be enjoying himself enormously.

Station Manager Bruce Robb, explains the mission at Blossom Point. "We provide data that will allow computation of an orbit and collect information from the satellite's instruments. Goddard schedules each station as to when it should take a pass. Schedules which come in via the teletype also give us information as to where the satellite will be in time and azimuth in relation to this station. Preliminary calculations are made before each launch, and if all goes according to plans, they know quite precisely where it will be, and when."

Bruce Robb, who has been with this station since 1958, explains that there are about forty people on station—minus five who are temporarily in the Moligossi Republic, Madagascar, with their trailer systems. "All shots from the Cape pass over Moligossi and right now our people are there to track the Canadian-built satellite, which was launched jointly by the United Kingdom and the United States." Robb produces a postcard received from his fellow sky ranger in Madagascar. The message says, "Just changed rooms. Now have bath *and* path," indicating that western living standards are often hard to come by in such areas.

But now it is time for a coffee break. Because of its remoteness, each station includes a cozy kitchen with stove, sink, refrigerator, cupboards, and dishes. As the coffee brews we learn that personnel bring their own lunches. "Lots of times you'll find people in here cooking steaks."

Dick Stone, Maintenance and Operations Supervisor, joins us during the break. He discusses living conditions for the personnel. "Most of us live in old farm houses or in La Plata. I guess housing is our biggest problem. Our children take a school bus but its an hour-long ride each way. Another

NASA ECHO COMMUNICATIONS SATELLITE

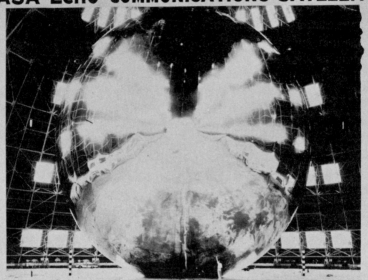

DIAMETER: 100 FT.   WEIGHT: SATELLITE 130 LBS.
                    INFLATION MATERIAL 30 LBS.
CONSTRUCTION: 0.0005 INCH THICK PLASTIC FILM COATED
              WITH VAPOR DEPOSITED ALUMINUM

L-100

problem is shopping. We don't dare forget any important items of food because its a twenty-five to thirty-mile trip to the nearest decent-sized store."

Doesn't this annoy the sky rangers and their families?

Dick shrugs good-naturedly. "I guess you could call it an occupational hazard in field engineering."

We learn that the work schedules vary, but average about ten to fifteen passes a day. The maximum would be twelve in an eight-hour shift. It takes about two man-hours for each pass but much of this time is spent in checking equipment. Setting up for a pass takes about fifteen minutes.

Blossom Point is currently responsible for fifteen satellites. Some require telemetry work, some tracking and some, both. "It depends on how much information the experimenter wants to get out of the satellite," Dick explains.

"Bong, bong, bong . . ." sound the doorbell chimes.

Those chimes, we learn, are a kind of pleasant way of alerting the trackers for a pass. "Why have an ugly-sounding buzzer when chimes are just as effective?"

Here comes Echo II, the giant 100-foot sphere communications satellite!

The man with the headset, which allows him to be in direct contact with Goddard Space Flight Center, tunes up the audio monitor to amplify the sound. Now, we can hear air noises and if we close our eyes we can almost imagine what it is like to whizz around the earth in the supercold, near-vacuum of 1,000 miles altitude. Air noise sounds very much like a roaring surf and it seems incredible that two small pancake devices only one foot in diameter and one and a half inches thick could transmit useful information through that *scramble* of whooshes to our group here on earth.

"As soon as it gets quiet, we'll know we have it," the trackers say. Then, "Ah, there it is."

The whooshing sounds fade into the background as the modulation from Echo II comes through with squeaks and tones. The operator nods his head with recognition and satisfaction, for he has long since become adept at identifying the voice of one satellite from that of another. He can also tell if it is operating correctly and in this case Echo II was tuned in perfectly except for a few moments when its split injured side turned toward earth. And even as the squeaks and tones are being recorded so that important

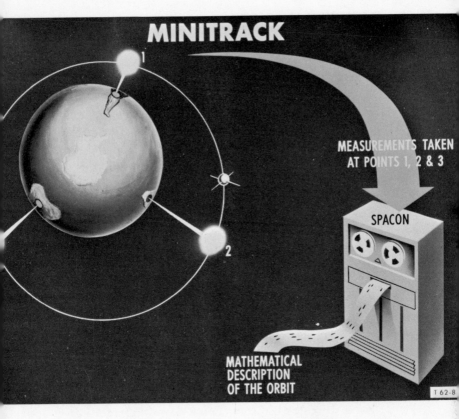

MINITRACK

MEASUREMENTS TAKEN AT POINTS 1, 2 & 3

SPACON

MATHEMATICAL DESCRIPTION OF THE ORBIT

T 62-8

data will be available for scientists, we can visually monitor the signal on the oscilloscope as the green trace dances on its black background.

"Had this pass been at night," Dick Stone explains, "we would have taken a picture with our MOTS (Miniature Optical Tracking System) camera." The large sky camera is located in a special shed that has a sliding roof. "We drive the camera in the direction opposite to the satellite in order to counteract the earth's rotation. The stars will show as bright spots on our plate but the satellite will be a long, streaking line. We can then correlate the plate to star charts and get a very precise measurement."

The squeaks and tones and beeps begin to fade away. Air noise whooshes through again and we hear the operators say, "Well, that's that."

Nowadays Echo II tracking is a fairly cut and dried process. But to get data from other satellites, such as Relay, is a more complicated process. "Early reduction of data used to be done by ear. Now we have Pulse Coded Modulation (PCM) that can sample various functions of the satellite, extract data from the interfering noise, and actually collect 8,000 bits of information *per second*. For instance, four pieces of information would be emerging from a composite signal. Each device filters out the desired information, even though to the ear it all sounds like air noise. From this, we can read what our 'end' instruments aboard the satellite are telling us.

" 'End' instruments can be a number of things: a position indicator, or a device to regulate solar batteries that will tell us the position of the satellite in relation to the sun. We learn what the temperature of the upper atmosphere is by asking the precalibrated temperature probe aboard the satellite."

Even though Blossom Point Minitrack station is the pioneer in the network, the sky rangers have not become bored with their unusual profession. "There is always a sense of excitement on a new launch," they say. This may be because they often see and test the satellite's transmitters before the launch, so they will become familiar with it. "It's never quite the same, though, until you track it in orbit." This station is also responsible for field testing much of the new equipment.

Although the Fort Myers, Florida, station is the formal school in Minitrack for Bendix and Goddard personnel, Blossom Point does on-the-job training of trackers for other stations.

5

Minitrack—in the Field

*The Black Box is only as good as the
morale of the people in the field.*
—CAPTAIN WINFRED BERG, USN

THIS adage of the space age may not have the
oriental charm of Confucius nor the brilliance of Shake-
speare but it is a pretty good indication of the responsibilities carried by our far-flung sky rangers. It suggests that
they must have a "special plus" (as psychologists would say)
to their personalities in order to adapt to unusual situations,
climates, altitudes, customs, deprivations, and temptations.
A sense of humor helps as well as a liking for people. The
ability and desire to become a part of the community is a
kind of trademark for the successful and dedicated sky
ranger. He will lecture at the local universities, lead the Boy
Scouts, serve on the Chamber of Commerce and generally
be a good neighbor. In South America, it must be noted,
over half the bachelors who serve there marry South American girls.

Trackers in the field must be able to get along with one
another, see the same faces day in and day out, hear the
same jokes, tolerate the same mannerisms, and still come

back for more. They must have a kind of pioneering spirit mixed with a conscience for work. Above all, trackers must have a love for adventure and an ingenuity that will allow them to "make do" and still enjoy life, wherever they happen to be.

Leister F. Graffis, President of Bendix Field Engineering Corporation explains the company's role in the satellite tracking business. "We have grown like Topsy since 1957. We now have Bendix Field Engineering employees all over the world. They join up with the understanding that they never know where they are to go next. Also, we hire on the site and bring in recruits from all over. Its a rugged life. The men go into it not for money but because of a real interest in their profession.

"We've been in this business for twelve or thirteen years and today there is no spot in the free world where we don't have people coming and going. There is nothing in space that Bendix is not responsible for in some tracking way. We know where everything is in space, both Russian and United States." (Note: Mr. Graffis is including the military network, NAVSPASUR, of which we shall hear later.)

In the early days of Minitrack stations, trackers felt much more isolated than they do today. NASA makes it a point to send out condensed news of launchings, and so on, to keep the men informed and to boost their morale. Since mail would take too long, this information is sent via teletype.

There is also SCAMA, a high quality voice arrangement, which, like a master switchboard, allows trackers in both manned flight stations and STADAN ones to talk with one another. Trackers can pick up a phone and talk anywhere in the world. All stations can hear but nobody except designated parties can talk. Arrangements can be made so that several or all stations can speak together. One interesting example of SCAMA's usefulness occurred during a manned flight. As the entire network listened, Hawaii doubted

Woomera's reading. It turned out that the storm over Australia had given Woomera a faulty reading and the matter was soon cleared up.

Trackers in far-flung areas know they are not forgotten by the "front office." Dutch Schildhauer at Bendix recalls the countdown of the Glenn flight. "Suddenly, there was a hold because of a station failure. The station was one of ours and I thought, Oh damn, somebody turned on an extra percolator and blew a fuse. However, the countdown resumed and I felt a lot better."

There are 1,200 people involved in tracking complexes and over 11,000 at stations apart from the Bendix Field Engineering home office at Owings Mills, Maryland. Some of these men are bright young geniuses of eighteen, others are experienced, mature sixty-year-olds. Personal and professional qualifications are what count.

A trip around to the NASA Minitrack stations is somewhat like flipping through copies of *National Geographic*, but Jerry Hunsicker, a veteran of six years of tracking, does it routinely in order to install new equipment and inspect existing gear.

Jerry's job comes as a kind of natural outgrowth of his work with General Electric in radar maintenance. In 1958, he switched to space work, went with Bendix to take a course in satellite tracking and then worked with the Army's "Microlock"—a tracking system which has since been discontinued.

One of Jerry's favorite stations is in St. John's, Newfoundland. This seacoast town east of Quebec, Canada, is certainly not a crossroads for world travelers. It is cold and there is much snow but it is one of the most beautiful of Old World cities. The station itself is located about twenty-five miles from town, over an almost impassable road, on a high bluff several hundred yards back from the ocean.

The station site was literally hacked out of the heavy

forests by Canadian contractors hired by NASA. Bendix people put up the antennae. It is now operated by nationals although there is always a sprinkling of American supervisors, repairmen, and periodic inspectors. These trackers from the "south" soon become proficient at such local sports as curling—a combination of bowling and shuffleboard, played on the ice. You see local people wearing curling medals as testimony to their skill at this national sport.

Another beautiful station is located in South Africa, fifty-five miles from Johannesburg in the bowl-shaped valley at Hartebeshok. The Jet Propulsion Laboratory (JPL) has facilities there also. These consist of two "dish" radars: a small one, with wide scanning capabilities, and a large one, which can "see" thousands of miles into space. In operation, the little dish scans the sky, spots the object, then tells the big dish where to look.

The Minitrack station consisting of the usual gray U.S. Steel pre-fab buildings is on the crest of the hill. The stations are run by South African nationals of Dutch and British descent, ITR/SCIR, a government agency similar to our NASA, and the labor force consists of tribal handymen. The entire station is self-contained, with its own power, living quarters, modern cafeterias, and recreation facilities. Since it is located at 11,000 feet, the climate is warm but not too humid. Carefully manicured lawns, pools, and brilliant flowers growing everywhere make it an exotic paradise from which to monitor man-made space objects.

Attacks on the labor force by leopards or other wild beasts are rare, but monkeys make regular forays into the food supplies. Jerry recalls the time Bendix was making a film called, *Our Personnel in Africa.* "There is a big floor-to-ceiling window, in back of which are the controls. We put our pet monkey at the controls for that shot. I'm not too sure how the gag went over with the front office."

At Winkfield, England, the station is located near Windsor not far from the Queen's summer castle. It is one of the "new" cities, with American-style shopping centers and supermarkets. London is about an hour's drive over pleasant country roads. The countryside is charming and quiet and Americans are generally well accepted. This was not always so, for, as is often the case, local people worried about all those antennae, radar, and hardware being installed near their peaceful homes. Was this to be a missile-launching site? Would their television sets and radios be disturbed? Jerry remembers how these problems were solved. "We began frequenting their local pubs, lunching with community groups and inviting them out to the station to watch the construction. Once people found out what we were really doing they were glad to have us there. Trackers are now an accepted group."

As has been said, sky rangers must be prepared to go anywhere in the world to carry out their mission—from the blue-white of Thule, Greenland, to the vibrantly colorful South Africa to the serene rolling countryside of Winkfield, England. They must also be prepared to spend time at such sites as Beatty, Nevada, where the bus stop doubles as a gambling casino. This station, used for tracking the X-15 experimental winged spacecraft is 90 miles from Tonopah and 120 miles from Las Vegas, and since it is at 9,000 feet altitude, there is snow in July. Bottled gas and water must be trucked in. Beatty of course is not a Minitrack station but rather a small Mercury system utilizing a radar acquisition aid (binoculars), radio telemetry, and diesels. The one word to describe living conditions here is—*miserable.*

East Grand Forks, Minnesota, is no picnic either. Located about 90 miles from the Canadian border and 200 miles from Minneapolis and St. Paul, the winter temperature scoots down to minus four degrees. The site itself is seven miles from public housing where a small basement apartment with no garage or storage space will cost about $130.00 a month. There is often so much snow that trackers cannot reach the station by road so they must be delivered to the rooftops by helicopter.

Even as sky rangers are shoveling snow and shivering in their boots at East Grand Forks, their fellow trackers are sweltering in temperatures that reach 122 degrees at the Goldstone Complex in the Mojave desert, California. With three inches of rain a year and a wind that often blows from twenty to fifty miles per hour, sky rangers could well wonder what ever possessed them to choose satellite tracking as a way of life. Yet, as they look around them, they are intrigued by the enormous array of equipment and what it can do—if it is competently maintained and operated. Is it worth the personal discomfort in order to live side by side with three 85-foot radar "dishes" whose beams reach thousands of miles out into space to monitor manned and unmanned vehicles of today and tomorrow? And what of the 40-foot circular dish which tells the big ones where to aim their beams? Yes, the trackers of JPL believe their adventures into space are sufficient rewards to make up for nature's meager endowments at Goldstone. Trackers who run the Goldstone all-purpose Minitrack station do not have the glamorous deep-space radars, yet they know their jobs are vitally important and—yes—it's well worth the heat, sand, wind, and sweat to carry out the mission.

Ah, but don't we hear the tantalizing sounds of Latin American music wafting our way from south of the border? *Si*, for here NASA still maintains several of the original Minitrack stations. Sky rangers in Quito, Ecuador, find themselves in a shutterbug's paradise of mountainous beauty 9,343 feet high in the Andes. A scant ten miles from the equator, Quito has flowers blooming all year round, and at

Minitrack station in Quito, Ecuador, is located at an altitude of 11,000 feet, a distinct hardship for sky rangers.

the tracking station, a two-hour's drive from town, palm and pine grow side by side. Sky rangers are put to stringent personality tests in Quito, for here they must know the language and culture of the area if they are to successfully fit in with the community. In a city of 400,000 population, only about 1,000 are North American, and of these, about 500 are Government employees and dependents. Kenneth G. Schlicher, veteran tracker explains that cliques and clubs among North Americans don't work out very well. "In fact, we don't even live in any special section of town. Because of the complete changeover in the way of life, some wives experience a kind of cultural shock. They just can't adjust, so of course they must be sent back to the States."

Schlicher, who is married to a Bolivian girl, explains that there is no central heating in their housing. "Families depend upon fireplaces or electric heaters for warmth. There is a great deal of poverty; fresh vegetables must be carefully cleaned and cooked before eating. But by far the most pressing problem for sky rangers in Quito is the altitude."

It has long been recognized that high altitudes (where oxygen molecules are less dense and air pressure is low) produce gross physiological and psychological changes in the human body. Trackers who are accustomed to working at lower altitudes find it difficult to pace their activities to allow for this oxygen starvation. Schlicher says, "Each person has a critical altitude, usually above eight or nine thousand feet; it varies with the individual. Some people never adapt." But here, at 11,000 feet, the Quito Minitrack station has been built; and here the sky rangers must work.

Trackers tell newcomers what they can expect in the way of symptoms; heart palpitations, shortness of breath, difficulty in sleeping, dizziness, headaches, and prolonged respiratory ailments. You experience forgetfulness so you write notes to yourself—only to lose the notes. Some men become belligerent for no apparent reason. At LaPaz, Bolivia, where the altitude is 13,700 feet, Schlicher recalls an episode when a mild-mannered pleasant little man suddenly went berserk and beat up a coworker. Afterwards he could offer no explanation as to why he did it. "We always keep oxygen bottles around the station for emergency use, particularly for visitors from the States."

As self-protection? Schlicher smiles his "no comment."

On the plus side in Quito, trackers can drive to any number of recreation areas to enjoy some of the finest outdoor sporting activities in the world. Swimming, golf, yachting, wild game hunting, tennis, and deep sea fishing are excellent the year round.

It can almost be said that if you close your eyes and stick a pin in the map, you will find sky rangers nearby monitoring the heavens. There, in Kano, Nigeria, trackers have encountered an unusual problem which they toss back to the home office. It seems they badly need a nonpoisonous rust inhibitor for their radiators. The reason for their concern is that trackers find the natives draining the boiling water from the radiators of NASA vehicles for use in making tea.

In Woomera, Australia, even now the strains of "Waltzing Matilda" come to greet us. No one of us who has ever watched a manned space flight on television could miss the name Woomera, for this tracking site always plays a major role in such dramatic shots.

Australia, land of primeval nature, of dusky green bush spiked with leathery growing things. D. H. Lawrence describes the hoary space of western Australia's bush country in *Kangaroo* : ". . . It is so aboriginal, out of our ken, and it hangs back so aloof. Yet you don't have the feeling of ugliness or monotony in the landscape. You get a sense of subtle, remote, formless beauty more poignant than anything ever experienced before."

Colors range from green-yellow, through salmon, to cochineal, and on the great dry salt lake that is Woomera there are purple shimmers against the horizon as the sun sets. The name itself means "a spear thrower used by the Australian aborigines" which is appropriate because Woomera began in 1946 as a missile test area for the British Commonwealth. During the IGY, the United States set up the Minitrack station and the Baker-Nunn camera—(of which we shall hear shortly), and subsequently, a Mercury network station along with a JPL big dish for deep space tracking.

It is a huge military installation for the combined operations of the British and Australian Army, Navy, and Air Force. Woomera calibrates its own Minitrack stations; its tracking personnel is primarily indigenous. At present, there is one Bendix field engineer and two NASA technicians working there. In all, about 100,000 people live and work at this sprawling Australian complex.

And then there are the kangaroos. As Jerry Hunsicker says, "They're all over the place."

Woomera is a key station, excellently run. Its personnel have always been interested in radio astronomy and their contributions to satellite tracking are invaluable. It is unique in that most of the trackers are Ph.D's or are about to receive their doctorates in the radio astronomy field.

6

The Satellite Tracking Camera—
The Pictured Truth

IT is twilight on the Polynesian island of Maui. On the soft sandy beach where dark waves curl and froth, a group of Hawaiian boys strum their ukeleles and raise their voices in delicious harmony. Their bronzed bodies sway with the ancient rhythms as a sarong-clad girl with an hibiscus tucked in her long black hair dances a traditional hula. Nearby in the shadows of the tall lava rocks, old Tutu, the maiden's grandmother nods her approval, for this is the way it should be danced. *Auwe!* Not like today, with all those tourists.

There are actually hundreds of Hawaiians attending the *luau* feast and in true Polynesian tradition, the *kalua* pig wrapped in banana and *ti* leaves, surrounded by yams, bananas, and other fruits and vegetables, is cooking in the pit. The moon and stars in the velvet sky overhead are the same heavenly bodies that guided the first Hawaiian settlers from their homeland in Tahiti centuries ago. How glorious it is to cling to the past, even if it is only for an evening of ancient feasting.

A few miles away, up the jungle-covered coastline, past the fragrance of the yellow and white ginger blossoms rises the majestic bulk of Haleakala Crater with its 10,000-foot-high peak. Often it is wreathed in clouds, but this evening, the clouds have disappeared. There is work to be done. Word has just been received at the SAO optical satellite tracking station on Haleakala that headquarters in Cambridge, Massachusetts, requests photos of the next satellite pass. Included in the teletype message is information about the expected time of the satellite's arrival and its corresponding positions in the sky. These predictions, the trackers know, were all made by the computer at the Smithsonian Astrophysical Observatory, from data sent in from other stations or from NASA, or from both.

In contrast to the balmy tropical breezes at sea level, the temperatures on the mountain are brisk and chilly, particularly at twilight, but this is when the optical trackers really come into their own—at dusk and dawn. These are the hours when the giant sky cameras can photograph a satellite against a star background so that scientists will have precise measurements with which to work. When weather conditions are right, at dusk and dawn, no other tracking device can offer such accuracy. The photos must be taken at the time when the earth is in darkness, but when the sun still illuminates the satellite.

The sky ranger slips on a windproof jacket and heads for the observatory that houses the Baker-Nunn camera. The protective roof slides back and the tracker aims his camera lense towards the sky at the starting point. He cannot see the satellite with his naked eye so he depends on his master clock to tell him when to press the button which starts the camera.

There is the signal!

The camera begins shooting pictures, one after another,

as the satellite streaks across the sky; and as the satellite moves, the gigantic camera keeps pace.

The sky ranger takes his precious film and develops it. What does he see as he holds it up to the light? A tiny pinpoint of light on a black background of stars, which appear as *streaks*. Scientists can now measure the position of the satellite, using a fixed-star background, and note the exact moment each picture was taken. The time, accurate to one-thousandth of a second, is automatically printed on

The pictured truth. Optical tracking produces invaluable photographs for scientific study. Here, earth's natural satellite, the moon, shares the predawn sky of October 16, 1957, with the third-stage rocket of Sputnik I. Its trail crosses the star Chi^2 Orionis; stars in Gemini are in the top of the field.

each photograph, by means of a slave clock built inside the camera and driven by a master crystal clock at the station.

The sky ranger at the remote Haleakala station, Maui Island, Hawaii, knows he has important information which must be gotten back to headquarters, Cambridge. In this case he uses the telegraph. At Cambridge, the results are fed into the electronic computer which prints out the corrected elements for the satellite's orbits. With these new predictions, word can be telegraphed to other stations which will be requested to make photographs of the next pass.

Meanwhile, down on the beach, it is *kau kau*, a time for feasting on pig and poi, for the blowing of the conch shell and for romantic mingling with the past. Were the guests aware of the tense drama with tomorrow which had just taken place so near to them? Probably not, for optical tracking today is in many respects a silent service. However, this was not always so.

At the same time that the radio interferometer system, Minitrack, was going through its teething processes during the IGY, a parallel or back-up system of optical tracking was being developed by the Smithsonian Astrophysical Observatory (SAO). SAO's Director, Dr. Fred L. Whipple had been involved in one of the early proposals to put a satellite into orbit (Project Orbiter) the diameter of which was to be thirty inches. Later, when Project Vanguard was settled upon, optical tracking plans had to be scaled down to twenty inches. As we have seen, the first Vanguard satellite, the "grapefruit," was only six inches in diameter; the image to be photographed was about twenty microns—or *one-fourth* the diameter of a human hair.

Could any camera be developed by man with such a capability? Since SAO had been assigned the responsibility for optically tracking the artificial satellite during the IGY, they were determined to succeed. Once the cameras were developed, they would be situated at key locations around the globe. They, along with hundreds of volunteer "Moon-watchers," would determine the exact orbital path of the satellite; record, analyze, and distribute the orbital information to other scientists throughout the scientific world.

But where does one begin?

Well, there was in existence, the super-Schmidt camera that astronomers had used for tracking meteors, but it could never meet the strict requirements of tracking a man-made satellite streaking like a 30-caliber bullet across the sky. To assist Dr. Whipple in the early stages of planning, Dr. J. Allen Hynek took leave as Professor of Physics and Astronomy at Ohio State University to become director of the optical tracking program.

Among the prime requirements laid down for the now famous Baker-Nunn camera was that it must have a second shutter in order to photograph a clock at the same time it photographed the satellite. This clock would have to be accurate to one millisecond.

It was a herculean task for Dr. James G. Baker, then a consultant to the Perkin-Elmer Corporation, to design a new optical system for the camera. This system would not be used for just one, but for twelve huge cameras, each of which would cost about $100,000, so there would have to be a reasonable chance of its being manufacturable. After much calculating and study, Dr. Baker decided he needed a corrector cell consisting of three lenses. At the same time he took into consideration Dr. Whipple's requirement that the lenses allow maximum passage of ultraviolet rays.

The search began for just the right optical glass, and Dr. Baker finally found it in the catalog of the German manufacturer Schott. KzFS-2 was chosen, along with a second glass, SK-14. The mirror, Pyrex, developed by Corning Glass, was another important element to be chosen.

Once the critical decisions were made, the next steps were

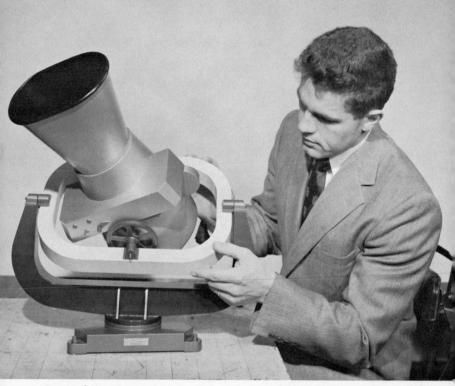

Dr. Karl G. Henize demonstrates with ⅙-size model of three-axis Baker-Nunn Schmidt-type telescope camera used to photograph the U.S. earth satellite in orbit. Dr. Henize was astronomer in charge of the twelve stations set up in all parts of the world by the Smithsonian Astrophysical Observatory, Cambridge, Massachusetts.

manufacture and transportation. Dr. Baker felt that even though the Schott Company was in Germany, they should still manufacture the large glass discs for the lenses, because margins for error were so slight. Here is where the Military Air Transport Service (MATS) entered the picture, with their huge aircraft to carry the precious cargo from Germany to the Perkin-Elmer Corporation in Norwalk, Connecticut, for the grinding of lenses.

Meanwhile, another design problem loomed up. Since, by any stretch of the imagination, a satellite would not remain stationary, neither should a tracking camera. Drs. Whipple and Hynek sought a solution from Joseph Nunn who came up with an oscillating base, placing the camera in a gimbal ring which would allow it to turn on three axes.

With the camera lenses and mounting checked off the list, Dr. Whipple and Hynek turned to the next requirement —the timing system. Arrangements were made for a radio to receive time signals put out by WWV, the National Bureau of Standards station in Beltsville, Maryland. These signals would feed into a Norrman crystal clock which would in turn feed into the "slave" clock inside the camera. In tests, this timing system deviated only one ten-thousandth of a second over a six-hour period.

One of the more interesting aspects of the development of the Baker-Nunn cameras is the similarity between them and Vanguard itself, which the cameras were designed to track. In each case there was no laboratory model or proto-type put on display for scientists and engineers to agree or disagree with.

The Pasadena firm of Boller and Chivens was responsible for manufacture of the mechanical components and their subsequent integration with the optical system. In each case the components came together on the drawing board—were unified and put to work. With Vanguard, as we have seen, there was serious trouble before compatibility was finally established. With the Baker-Nunn cameras it was sweetness and light from the very beginning and it has been said that these cameras will go down in history as true triumphs of American craftsmanship. With the components of all twelve cameras, mass-produced in the same manner as an auto-mobile, a ship, or any ordinary day-to-day product, an en-tirely new and fascinating concept of scientific genius, coupled with practical know-how, was introduced to the field of science. To honor Dr. Whipple specifically for his work in creating this system, President Kennedy in June 1963 awarded him "the highest honor the Government can bestow upon a career employee"—The President's Award.

The cameras in operation do require acquisition by radio or by visual means. In other words, camera operators need to know in which direction to point their lenses in order to photograph the satellite as it passes from horizon to horizon. What happens is, the scientists at SAO Headquarters in Cambridge gather all possible information of the satellite's orbit, from Minitrack stations and from volunteer Moonwatch teams around the world (we now have acquisition aids). Using this information, as well as previous Baker-Nunn observations, which are the best source of supply because of their accuracy, the scientists can then compute the orbit and make new predictions as to altitude, azimuth, angular velocity at the point of culmination, and track angle. These data are then teletyped in code to the man with a camera. It becomes a cumulative thing because the more observations made, the more SAO knows about the satellite's behavior. In other words, the orbit is continually being refined.

Once the sky ranger has taken his photos he develops them in his dark room and then projects them on an enlarged star chart. He gets his fix on the satellite to an accuracy of one to three minutes of arc and one-tenth of a second in time. He quickly cables this information to SAO, which then feeds it into the IBM 7090 computer. This computer can, for example, take eight days' work from the field and in two minutes, compute the orbit.

Under suitable conditions, each individual camera can track different objects that come by at two to five minutes apart. Again, depending on the stellar magnitude of the object, the angular velocity, and the sky brightness, the Baker-Nunn can track:

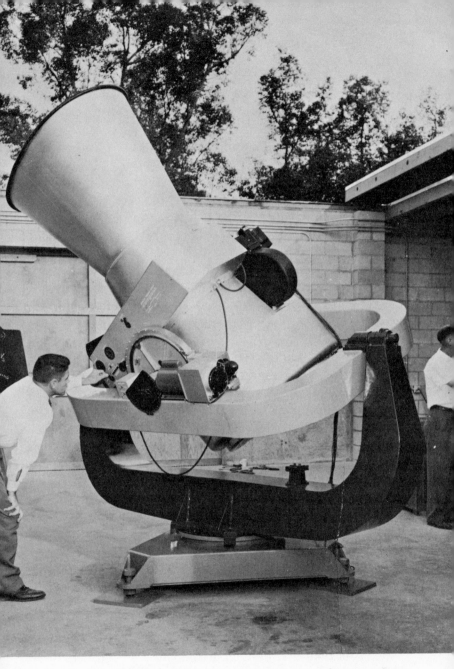

One of twelve specially designed Baker-Nunn Schmidt-type telescope cameras, the camera most capable of photographing artificial earth satellites as they orbit around the world. These giant cameras, ten feet high by eight feet wide, were set up at tracking stations strategically located around the world, organized and directed by the Smithsonian Astrophysical Observatory, Cambridge, Massachusetts.

1. a 20-inch sphere to 2,000 miles in
   1,000-mile altitude orbit or higher
2. 1,200 miles in a 500-mile orbit
3. 600 miles in a 200-mile orbit

Remember, we are speaking of a *20-inch* sphere!

For a larger object, of say 8 feet, the camera can photograph it up to 240,000 miles, if it is not near the moon. Dr. Fred Whipple says that "to date, no earth-orbiting satellite has exceeded the capability of the Baker-Nunn cameras." Going back a few years, it was indeed a triumph to successfully photograph the tiny 6-inch Vanguard at a distance of 3,000 miles. This feat has been described as being similar to photographing a .30 caliber bullet in flight from 200 miles distance. The Baker-Nunn Sky Rangers actually photographed the "Paddle Wheel" satellite at 14,000 miles.

As with all tracking systems, the Baker-Nunn cameras have advantages and disadvantages. On the plus side, they do not require radio transmission from the satellite, as does Minitrack, and have in many cases been able to track satellites whose radios have ceased to operate. By far their most important advantage over other systems is their astounding precision. Says Edmund Buckley, "The Baker-Nunns have been excellent for certain scientific uses such as dynamic geodesy. All their work paid off with the spectacular studies in bulges in the atmosphere and careful detail of the *drag* of vehicles in the upper atmosphere."

Dr. Luigi Jacchia of SAO explains his views on the camera's contribution to the world of science. He describes the three phases of optical tracking. "Our pre-Sputnik knowledge of the upper atmosphere density and solar light pressure and other factors affecting the satellite's motion was so scanty that our first position predictions almost had to be in error. Indeed, the very degree of inaccuracy of those early predictions was an indication of how much there was to be learned about the causes of the inaccuracy. There were so many things we did not understand well enough . . . so many things making the satellite's motion erratic and prediction difficult. This infuriated the camera crews but clearly showed the need for the pictures which they were having some difficulty in getting. They did catch some, and observations were made. Scientists were able to study the satellite's motion and thus predict it better.

This photo shows the Explorer 19, a 12-foot rigidized balloon satellite. The photograph was dated January 5, 1964, but the station location is unknown. The satellite data was used by Dr. Jacchia of the Observatory staff for determination of atmospheric heating over the poles.

"The second phase was when we had more satellites to track. It became a mass production. Tracking stations that in 1958 had gone for weeks without catching a single satellite began scoring success with one or more a night. In 1959, 6,524 observations were made, and in 1960, 12,249.

"The third phase which we are in at present is one of specialization. Cameras now follow specified satellites only and photograph them over longer arcs. We have simultaneous observations with several cameras which have been synchronized, photographing the same satellite at the same time. With this technique we can calculate the distances between cameras; usually over ocean distances. It is very hard to measure over water and there may be an error of hundreds of yards. (Pacific navigators found errors of several miles.) Precision photos locating a satellite against the stars to a time accuracy approaching one-thousandth of a second will bring possible errors in transocean distances down to a few yards only."

In the early days of inaccurate predictions, important sky photographs were often hard to come by and this acquisition requirement is one of the camera's disadvantages. Another limitation is weather. Clouds or storms will prevent the optical sky ranger from taking his photos. And, as has been said, his "shooting" hours are limited to dawn and dusk. The cameras cannot produce data in "real time"—as it happens. Even so, they have been invaluable for the purposes for which they were designed.

Today, SAO cameras contribute information to both NORAD (North American Defense Command—SPADATS) and NASA. They satisfactorily photograph more than 2,000 satellite passages each month, an output that is the result of constant improvement in station efficiency. On an average basis, out of each 100 passages predicted, about 35 are observed, 40 are lost because of weather, and, for miscellaneous technical reasons, the remainder are not observed.

7

The Worldwide Optical
Tracking System

THE beloved Will Rogers once said, "There is a lot of difference in pioneering for gold and pioneering for spinach." Our sky rangers of a few short years ago could point out that there is also a lot of difference in pioneering for satellite tracking.

When it was decided that twelve camera sites would be needed (only three were to be on United States soil) for the SAO to fulfill its tracking mission for the IGY, in 1956, Dr. Whipple presented his problem to participating members of the IGY meeting in Barcelona, Spain.

Would it be possible to forget politics, military suspicion, nationalism, and diplomatic headlines so that Americans might move bag and baggage into these countries, and assist the great scientific effort of the IGY?

The response was an overwhelming Yes. And there would be all possible help and cooperation right down the line, not only from the scientific communities in the various countries but from the governments as well. The station

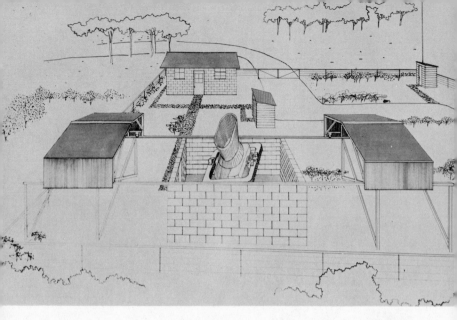

Drawing of a typical photographic satellite-tracking station. Twelve of these stations were constructed in strategic places around the world. The heart of the station is the Baker-Nunn telescope-camera shown in the center foreground. The roof has been opened to allow the camera full view of the sky. This camera is used to photograph satellites, and from the 55-millimeter film photographs, precise measurements are made to determine satellites' orbits around the earth.

sites chosen were Cordoba, Argentina; Woomera, Australia; Curacao, Netherlands West Indies; Naini Tal, India; Mitaka, Japan; Arequipa, Peru; Bloemfontein, South Africa; Cadiz, Spain; Alamogordo (White Sands), New Mexico; Maui, Hawaii, and Jupiter, Florida.

In retrospect, it is difficult to realize that the "impossible" task of putting up twelve complex tracking stations in such distant areas was actually accomplished in a mere eighteen months. Each of the stations included a building with a sliding roof to house the camera, an administration building, a small building for housing tools and supplies, a dark room for film processing and reduction, and communications facilities for teletype, telephone, and mail. In addition to the problems of shipping the huge, delicate cameras over thousands of miles of land and ocean, about ten tons of equipment were needed for each station.

And what about the men who would run the stations from sunset to sunrise, day in and day out? What sort of employment rules could be followed in selecting personnel that were technically skilled and trained, dependable without being dependent on others for on-the-spot decisions, willing to be alone and yet capable of getting along with people of various nationalities and colors? As pointed out in Shirley Thomas's book, *Satellite Tracking Facilities, Their History and Operation*, "Each man would have to possess the reliability of a banker, the fortitude of a lighthouse keeper, the skill of a carpenter, the understanding of a general scientist, and the enthusiasm of a man eager to take part in this first space development. It was a long and seemingly contradictory set of requirements."

Dr. Fred Whipple summed it up with "The most important single characteristic these men must have is a real pioneering spirit."

The call went out to scientific journals, professional groups, and institutions. But important was the word-of-mouth recruitment. Almost from the very beginning, the group that was carefully screened, trained, and sent to the far corners of the earth became a fiercely loyal family, tied together by an underlying spirit of determination to succeed in spite of all obstacles. At first, their jobs were lonely, until station complements could be expanded. Often, station managers were plagued by money problems and the feeling that nobody back at headquarters knew what they were going through, or even cared. Communications were a problem and early orbital predictions were often incorrect, so that a night's work might prove valueless. But they stuck it out during those early years, so that, today, each man can remember with pride the part he played in establishing our excellent worldwide optical tracking system.

But perhaps we should visit our first pioneer sky ranger as he went about setting up his station during the IGY. His name is Sam Whidden and he was actually the first observer to be signed on by the Smithsonian. He had earlier been on the Harvard meteor project and was already something of an expert in the processing of film to be used in the Baker-Nunn camera. He married Martha Holt of the Cambridge staff, and together they set off to . . .

Naini Tal, India. Roll that name off your tongue. Naini Tal . . . it has a musical ring to it. Naini Tal, land of mystery and enchantment, the Bengal Lancers and Gunga Din. What a lovely place for a honeymoon. But where is it?

Tucked away in the Kumoan Hills on the lower ranges of the Himalaya mountains lies the Uttar Pradesh State Observatory. It occupies a vantage point on Manora Peak, and

SMITHSONIAN ASTROPHYSICAL OBSERVATORY NETWORK (SAO)

Sky rangers operate the excellent Baker-Nunn cameras at far-flung stations around the world.

at a height of 6,400 feet above sea level it would be linked to the satellite tracking station of Naini Tal by a ten-mile road.

This station, like those at Australia and Japan, was to be entirely under the direction of the local authorities, although Sam was to be the advisor for the initial construction and establishment. The station's independence had to be strictly maintained in order for Parliament to approve the financial support. (The observatory allotted one-eighth of its total budget for satellite tracking.)

Another prickly problem facing Sam was the presence of his assistants, who happened to be American military personnel of the Army Map Service. Some Indians wondered if this were the beginning of an invasion of their soil. Somehow the arrival in February, 1958, of Sergeants Erskine and Simonds was justified in the interest of science, the IGY, and the fact that they wouldn't be around Naini Tal very long.

Records show that the tracking camera was shipped to India the latter part of March. Why then was it the 29th of August, 1958, before the observers were able to capture 1958 DELTA I?

Why indeed?

Consider the weather. The average rainfall in this area is 105 inches per year, and when the monsoon season arrives in June, the heavens literally open up. Some days there pours down as much as five or six inches of rain in a twelve-hour period. With the monsoons come the leeches, snakes, scorpions, and other odd-looking creatures. Sam and his people were often forced to march stoutly down the mountain and back, three miles each way, because roads were washed out and could not handle motor traffic. He finally got disgusted and bought a horse.

Weather was only one of the problems. Another was pilferage. Well over a ton and a half of steel disappeared from the docks at Bombay before it could be gotten up the mountain to the station site. Included in this grand theft was the specially prefabricated steel roof which would provide smooth opening of the camera house top.

What to do? The house had to have a roof in order to protect the precious camera from the weather. After much dickering, Sam managed to get some more steel and to find workers to cut the new camera house roof and construct it. It was finally hoisted onto the building by rope—and human muscle.

But there was equipment yet to be brought to the station. The Indians suggested hiring coolies to carry it up the mountain by the armload. This system, along with the two chain hoists and some rope which Sam got hold of, did the trick.

Meanwhile, Sam's bride was having her own brand of trouble. Since Naini Tal is a resort town where prices are high, especially for "rich" Americans, she found herself spending about ninety percent of their income—about $450.00—just to get along.

Instead of a modern gas range, Martha found a cook who would prepare the meals over a little charcoal pit. He tried very hard to serve them American-style food but was sadly limited by what was available in Naini Tal's open air supermarket (dogs wandered freely in the littered streets; vegetables were unprotected and dirty; meat was so thickly covered by flies that its origin was undeterminable). Martha did manage to shop by mail through the Embassy Commissary in Delhi for a few American type groceries, to the tune of some $50.00 a month.

The cook, incidentally, had tuberculosis as did about thirty percent of the Indian population. Since he was such a good cook and such a nice fellow, the Whiddens had his condition treated, rather than discharge him.

In spite of earth's atmospheric dust, the SAO station at Organ Pass, N. M., photographed the entire lunar eclipse of Dec. 30, 1963.

The bride's romantic dream house boasted a half-dozen light sockets, dirt, four cold-water taps, a sofa, dirt, a few chairs and tables, two three-foot tin bathtubs (portable), the charcoal cooking pit, dirt, mud walls, and some rugs.

Letters to and from the Smithsonian were a great joy. Martha wrote home to Cambridge, "In order not to go blind reading letters from Cambridge we have installed a few more light fixtures, and in order that we may survive the winters to carry out our mission for Smithsonian, we have installed the required separate electrical circuit for heater plugs. We also have bought some furniture and it is our pathetic little dream to install a flush toilet (which we will not be able to afford). We have gone so far as to install a GI-type shower in order to adequately romove from our bodies the filth which is everywhere. . . ."

To outward appearances, the Whiddens' status was roughly equivalent to that of a rather middle-class Indian Government official. Their income of course was larger, but they used theirs in typically American fashion—to improve their living standard rather than for show such as hiring more servants.

Anyone for tracking in India?

No? Well, how about Iran then?

The eighth station to be established in the network of optical tracking stations was located in Shiraz, a city of some 150,000 people, nestled in a valley at an elevation of 5,300 feet among snow-capped mountains that reach as high as 8,000 feet. The tracking station is on rising ground, about three miles northwest of the city, on land owned by the Nemazee Hospital, and is ranked as the fourth most popular tourist attraction in the area. During the ten days of Now-Ruz, Islam's New Year, the station will welcome up to 1,250 visitors. The city of Shiraz was selected as a station site because, in addition to having clear skies, it is situated on latitude 32 degrees from the equator, which is approximately in the middle of low-inclination satellites' routes.

The first American observer to arrive at the station was Morgan Thomas. With his family, he set up housekeeping Iranian style. Morgan is yet another example of the type employed by SAO during the early years. An extremely avid amateur astronomer, Morgan was, by profession, a technical photographer for Boeing Aircraft, before he joined SAO. As a sideline, he produced documentary films on natural history.

On the scene at Shiraz he learned that the Universities of Teheran and Shiraz would assume part of the construction costs of the buildings, and would arrange for leasing land from the Nemazee Hospital. All seemed to be in good order and construction begun, when, almost overnight, rumors began to fly. "Mr. Morgan is building a launching site!" Fortuately, the U.S. Information Service was able to place a good and timely article in several of the Iranian papers, which explained to the people that the tracking station would be for peaceful scientific research rather than for war.

Morgan looks back with mixed emotions on those days of setting up the station at Shiraz. It was a good life to be in a country so rich in history, where in 331 B.C., Alexander destroyed the great Persian Empire and burned the city of Persepolis; where during the IGY distinguished gentlemen such as Senator Hessaby extended gracious Persian hospitality. (During a nine-course dinner at the Hessaby home, the family pet, a lovely buff-colored gazelle roamed the living room, eating candy from dishes and begging for nuts.) But it was an exhausting life.

Morgan often found himself working twelve to sixteen hours a day, first in preparation for the arrival of the electronic time standard and the interim theodolite, and later, the tracking camera. Also, from the very beginning, Shiraz

Sky rangers at SAO station in Shiraz, Iran, often found themselves working twelv
to sixteen hours a day at the beginning of the program.

station received poor predictions and this condition continued through most of 1958. Morgan Thomas, and later,
Charles "Chick" Capen, learned that the best predictions
came from Cameron, at the South Africa station, but even
these were not enough. What to do? The only solution at
that time was to compute by hand, utilizing the local moonwatch team and back-plotting the sky position in order to
locate the satellite. The following day, its expected position
with reference to the background star field could be deter-

mined to approximately a minute's accuracy. An hour before the expected satellite passage, the observers would set up the camera and locate the star field with the aid of a Norton's or Webb's Star Atlas, using the M-17 finder telescope on the Baker-Nunn camera. They could then backtrack 10 or 20 degrees, and wait for the satellite.

It was hard, painstaking work to compute in such a manner, but at long last the Mark IV Ephemeris came to the rescue and corrected the prediction situation. Morale rose tremendously. Gone were the Rube Goldberg systems of "make-do" and by 1959 Alpha, there were no more difficulties with predictions.

As observers wrestled with prediction problems they also ran head-on into communications blocks: that is, no telephones. Predictions were received and observations transmitted over the ministry of posts and telegraph lines, using the local post office facilities. Incoming signals were delivered to the home of Mr. Capen, for example, and outgoing were hand-carried to the city post office. No facilities were available for receiving or sending signals in the all-important evening hours. This problem disappeared with the installation of a radio teletype link.

Slowly but surely the Shiraz, Iran, station was whipped into fine shape. The operation is streamlined now . . . but wait. Station notes from Sam Tishler at Iran say, "Really never a dull moment here. Last week on two nights our drivers saw several wolves below the station and observers heard them howling in the distance. Hass Hajeb (Iranian observer) surprised everyone with his ability to call to the animals and have them answer."

Four days later. "The wolves that were sighted last week are still around. Hass comes to work armed to the teeth with a 4-inch jackknife. He locks the camera-house doors between passes, on the theory that the wolves might decide to come in where it's warm. I think that he doesn't want to get a horrible surprise."

Perhaps, after all, the pioneering spirit at Shiraz has not disappeared. We know it still exists at the Villa Dolores, Argentina, station. Don Tingle had quite a time of it the other night, when, at about 10 P.M., a local species of rattleless rattlesnake found its way into the photoreduction room. With no appropriate weapon at hand and his fellow observer, Anton, out of earshot in another building, Tingle sloshed the reptile with carbon tetrachloride and bombarded it with film cans until help arrived. Anton wandered back in time to deliver the *coup de grace* with a heavy board and then began speculating on the validity of the popular belief that such snakes travel in pairs. About forty minutes after midnight, a similar reptile, but larger, appeared, cruising in the driveway, perhaps seeking his mate. Eschewing nonsense, Anton turned a flashlight on the snake while Tingle dispatched it with a single blow on the head with a length of wood. "Please," the observers reported, "communicate our order for one snakebite kit."

Aside from rattleless rattlesnakes, locusts, swarms of ants, and so forth, trackers at Villa Dolores find peace with the night skies and pleasure in the warm Argentine sunshine. There is swimming, fishing, boating, hiking, and horseback riding to liven up their somewhat quiet, isolated life in the small rural town. The nearest good-sized city, Córdoba, is accessible by air only in the summer months. Otherwise, it is a long, treacherous, bumpy bus ride over a washboard dirt-surface road for 100 miles. The station is built of locally made red brick, painted a cream color, and is plastered inside so that it blends pleasantly with other Spanish-style architecture. It is located in a historically romantic setting near the Arroyo Seco (dry gulch) and Boca del Rio, an area once the home of ancient Indian tribes. Surrounding the station are rolling foothills, covered with thick native thorn and wiry brush. It is a country of ranches and small farms, of citrus and olive groves, of fruit orchards and vegetable patches. Brilliant, gorgeous flowers grow everywhere.

Quiet, serene, traditional, and very much *mañana* in personality, Villa Dolores has found itself in the peculiar position of hosting tomorrow, while its heart is still in the past. Even though land and assistance were provided through the Astronomical Observatory of the University of Córdoba during the IGY establishment of the station, these blessings

This photo, taken January 28, 1964, shows an unidentified part from the Echo II launching, possibly a canister half. The object can be seen at the tip of the second from right) broken-line dash in the star trail.

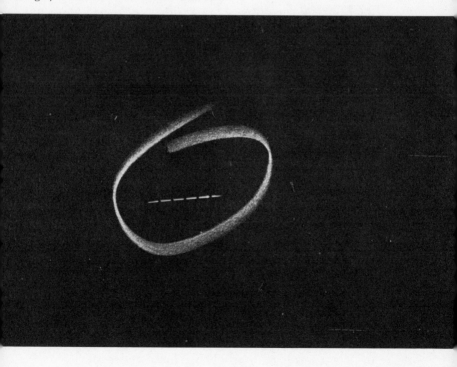

were not enough to counteract local opposition. Walter Lang, whose responsibility it was to set up the South American stations, had no end of problems with the unstable political situation, which included active Communist resistance. Almost every action he took had to be referred to Buenos Aires, and communication was at its poorest—four hours was considered a normal time delay. There was constant agitation by Communists. Payment of workmen was delayed or withheld even when the money was available. Not one of the completion dates was met. The foreman of the workers stated several times that he would finish the station when he felt like it, and that there was no rush involved. Then a mysterious force started a fire which destroyed the inside of the camera house, although fortunately the $100,000 camera had not yet been installed. While Walt Lang was pushing for completion of the really important things like power, darkroom facilities, and camera house, the workmen proceeded with such nonessentials as fences, a flagpole, gates, and fancy trim work. Frustration was at a peak, with hair-tearing situation after situation piling up. But, the job got done.

Argentina was the eleventh station to be established, and although the camera was shipped on May 14, 1958, it was not until July 10 of that year that the first observation was made of 1958 DELTA II.

The Japanese have always had a genius for optics and astronomy. The Baker-Nunn camera couldn't be more their cup of *sake*. Their station in Mitaka, forty miles outside of Tokyo was established quite painlessly through the co-operation of Dr. Takesi Nagata, Secretary to the Japanese Committee for the IGY, and Dr. Masasi Miyadi, Co-ordinator for the IGY and Director of the Tokyo Astronomical Observatory. SAO's Martin Burkhead and Aubrey Stennett supervised installation of the camera, but from then to now it has been a purely Japanese endeavor.

Woomera, of course, is Australian all the way, with an occasional American observer stationed there to assist in the operation of the station. And then there is the little town of San Fernando, near Cadiz, in Spain, where yet another tracking camera has been installed. Here, members of the *Guardia Civil* appear at the station in their patent-leather cocked hats, green uniforms, and automatic rifles, to ask if they may be shown around. Burro carts piled high with freshly caught shark amble sleepily along the dusty roads, while señoritas congregate beneath ancient fig trees in the enclosed gardens to gossip and sew. The Spanish station, fourth in the network, received excellent logistical support from the Rota Naval Air Base, forty miles away. Arrangements for the establishment of the station were initiated in mid-1956 with M. C. Herero of the Batelle Institute in Madrid, and early in 1957, with Admiral de la Puente, Director of the Spanish Naval Observatory.

And so, station by station, the Baker-Nunn cameras clicked into operation. Joining the electronic ears of Minitrack stations as they strained for the tone of the satellite's tiny radio transmitters, the indented eyes of the precision tracking cameras pierced the night sky to record the flight of the speeding satellites. And with these professional groups of trackers were hundreds of dedicated volunteer amateur astronomers around the world.

This remarkable program of SAO's was called "Project Moonwatch."

8

Project Moonwatch

THE concept of a world network of unpaid observers to visually track artificial satellites during the IGY was first proposed by Dr. Fred Whipple in 1955. "It will be a new global science sport," he said, "and its purpose will be to help acquire newly launched satellites, to back up radio tracking systems (Minitrack) and to observe 'swirl-ins,' or dying satellites, as they plunge into the lower atmosphere."

The idea caught the public fancy, for here at last was a chance for the man on the street, the high school science student, the armchair stargazer, or the public-minded volunteer to render a great service to his country, to science, and to mankind. No longer would they be outsiders in the great space effort to orbit a satellite. It wouldn't cost much for each person to outfit himself and join the team. About twenty dollars would buy an appropriate telescope, and observing could be carried on in fields, backyards, or on school rooftops near home. Yes, it was a great idea, but how does one go about recruiting unpaid volunteers to sit through the cold nights and peer into the dark sky without leaving their posts?

Bulletins were published and distributed to amateur astronomers throughout the United States, and to selected astronomical groups overseas. The publication *Sky and Telescope* issued an invitation to amateur astronomers and other interested parties to share in the program. Within the United States, applications were to be made to SAO; and

Project Moonwatch caught the public fancy, for here at last was a chance for the man on the street, the high school science student, the armchair stargazer, the public-minded volunteer, to render great service to country, to science, and to mankind.

in foreign countries, prospective Moonwatchers could apply to SAO through their respective IGY Committees.

Dr. Armand Spitz, a prominent and ardent astronomer, was selected as coordinator of the U.S. Moonwatch teams. He spent the summer of 1956 touring the country and spreading the word about the volunteer visual program. "Each individual will carry a heavy responsibility toward the success of the total program. Each group, and every member of the group must be completely dependable if the sum of the observations is to achieve our purpose. . . ." were his words to interested amateur astronomers.

Further impetus was gained during the Barcelona Conference of the IGY, held in September, 1956. Through the delegates, all amateur astronomers and other interested persons were urged to participate in Moonwatch. At this conference, Dr. Sidney Chapman, President of the Special Committee for the IGY, announced that the United States and the Soviet Union were cooperating in their plans for artificial satellites, and that similar instruments and techniques would be used for tracking both American and Russian satellites.

Meanwhile, Dr. George Van Biesbroeck, veteran observer of the Yerkes Observatory and for over forty years actively engaged in observing double stars, comets, astroids, and solar eclipses, joined the program to provide scientific and technical advice. Leon Campbell joined SAO's staff at Cambridge to become Supervisor of Station Operations.

So great was the response to SAO's invitation to join Moonwatch that by October 4, 1957, when Sputnik I was launched, Project Moonwatch had approximately 225 teams scattered throughout the world. By far the most enthusiastic foreign response came from the Japanese, whose student groups were organized by experienced amateur astronomers. They formed thirty such teams. Elsewhere, there were ten

A Moonwatch team of Boy Scouts in the Philippines practice observing techniques with elbow telescopes.

in Argentina; five in Australia; six in Chile; two in Formosa; one each in Egypt, Denmark, the Belgian Congo, Iran, Mexico, Liberia, Netherlands West Indies, and India; two each in Italy, Peru, and the Philippines; four in the Union of South Africa, and ten in Germany.

But how does a Moonwatch team actually operate?

Basically, it is a team of observers, each of whom maintains continuous watch—during the observing interval—of a specified sky area on the celestial meridian. These areas overlap so the satellite cannot cross this "meridional fence" without being detected. The director of each station selects and recruits personnel, and assigns senior observers to man the main north-south or meridional line.

Each person on this line is assigned one specific area for which he is responsible. He must not leave his post during the observing session, even if another watcher suddenly shouts, "There it is!" because there is always the possibility of a misidentification.

It has always been serious business. It was particularly vital during the early days, when acquisition aids were limited and untried. Orbits were calculated on the basis of the Moonwatch team's observations. The effectiveness of the interim super-Schmidt, and later, Baker-Nunn, cameras around the world would have been seriously impaired had not the visual observer stayed faithfully at his post.

The number of observers required in any given group depended on the type of instrumentation available. It was generally accepted that thirty was a comfortable number.

Obviously, a precise observation of a satellite position in the sky is worthless unless the observer's geographical position is accurately known. For this reason, group leaders were advised to discourage the "lone wolf" observer, and to forward to SAO only the observations made at the site selected and registered for his particular group. Only then could the computing machine at the central computing center, with its predetermined geographical positions etched in its memory, produce accurate predictions.

Major technical problems facing the program involved selecting a suitable telescope, obtaining precision timing and accurately recording the satellite position in relation to the star background. To iron out these problems, Mr. G. R. Wright formed a pilot Moonwatch station at his home in Silver Spring, Maryland. A number of optical instruments were tested by his eager team of amateur astronomers. Three out of some thirty instruments tested met the requirements.

An instrument called Moonwatch monoscope was the

general-purpose favorite. The scope provided a 12½-degree field with reasonable image brightness and a magnification of 5.5x. It offered the best performance consistent with availability and low cost. Surprisingly enough, the parts cost less than twenty dollars, and all the optical elements were war surplus items which could be purchased through supply houses. The eyepiece chosen was a wide-angle Erfle of 1¼-inch focal length with a 68-degree field. The objective was 51 mm in diameter, with a focal length of 180 mm. Objective and eyepiece were mounted in an aluminum tube 8½ inches long. The back surface of the objective was approximately 7⅛ inches from the front surface of the eyepiece, thus providing a focusing range from 10 feet to infinity. A front surface aluminized or silvered mirror was mounted at a 45-degree angle in front of the objective. This arrangement permitted the observer to watch his assigned area of the sky with comfort, irrespective of its altitude above the horizon.

Cost was an important factor because no funds were available for providing instruments to the teams. It therefore became necessary for each individual member to procure or construct his or her own telescope, unless he was fortunate enough to gain support of local organizations or other interested groups. About half the observers built their own scopes; the remaining group purchased the Edscope, which was available commercially for about fifty dollars.

Sponsorship of Moonwatch teams came from many sources: Hughes Aircraft Company, Tucson; Kiwanis Club and Edgewater Beach Hotel in Chicago: Wichita 7-Up Bottling Company; Indiana Astronomical Society; Minneapolis-Honeywell Regulator Company and Wilke Foundation, Minneapolis; Cleveland News; Franklin Institute, Texas A & M Research Foundation; Fort Worth Astronomical Society and the Recreation Department of Convair, and many others. Stations were located on tops of buildings, in backyards, in vacant lots, at observatories and factories, at universities in the north, south, east, and west around the world.

Most of the stations planned to use a typical Moonwatch monoscope, permitting them to track 8th-magnitude objects. However, fainter satellites or brighter satellites at greater apogee distance might possibly be launched. Therefore, an instrument of deeper penetration would be required to track them. With this in mind, a network of carefully selected Moonwatch stations was established at strategic locations around the world. They were equipped with 8-power M-17 Elbow Telescopes. These instruments have a 50-mm objective and a field of 2.4 degrees. They were supplied by the U.S. Naval Research Laboratories. Stations in this special network were located at Capetown, Johannesburg, and Pretoria, South Africa; at Kirkland AFB in Albuquerque, New Mexico; at the Naval Ordnance Test Station at China Lake, California; at Vincent AFB, Yuma, Arizona; and near Holloman AFB, Alamogordo, New Mexico.

Even as these stations were being set up, Moonwatch leaders were making vital decisions about such matters as timing. An inexpensive chronograph or stopwatch would do. Time would be checked periodically against accurate short-wave-radio time signals broadcast by WWV in the United States, WWVH in Hawaii, or some other national time service, depending on the location of the station. In the case of a chronograph, a satisfactory method of comparing radio and clock time is to register the radio time signal directly on the chronograph record. This allows measurement of the clock correction with at least as much accuracy as can be obtained in timing the observations.

The teams were also wrestling with the technical problem of accurately recording the satellite's position against the background of stars. This was solved by furnishing each station with a copy of the "Skalnate Pleso Atlas of the Heavens." In looking into his scope, the observer now had a background of stars, which formed an array of precise reference points against which satellite observations could be made.

There was yet another matter to be settled. If the volunteers manning the observation stations were to perform their jobs effectively, orbital predictions would have to be flashed to them daily. Communications proved to be the weakest link in the whole system. The expense of sending commercial telephone or telegraph messages to more than a thousand tracking stations across the country each and every day was out of the question. Who would come to the rescue? None other than volunteers of the Civil Air Patrol (CAP). Housewives, businessmen, lawyers, bankers, policemen—people from all walks of life who regularly serve with CAP—offered their services enthusiastically.

It was fortunate that one of the facilities maintained by the CAP is a well-disciplined communications network with sixteen years of training behind it. Numbering 13,000 individual stations, both fixed and mobile, coast to coast, manned by qualified volunteer operators, the CAP could and would handle the job.

Within twenty-four hours after CAP assistance was offered, the first orbital prediction of the Russian satellite was transmitted from Washington, D.C. The message was received at each of the fifty-two CAP wings, all forty-nine states, Hawaii, Puerto Rico, and the District of Columbia. Immediately, CAP operators began broadcasting the orbital predictions to squadron stations situated in each of the Moonwatch observation areas. In hundreds of communities all over the country, loyal citizens, from lawyers to schoolteachers, operating out of their homes, were alerted to establish the CAP network for the transmission of the tracking information. Civilians by day, uniformed volunteers by night, they generously lent their time and equipment to the cause of Project Moonwatch.

Immediately the all-important message was relayed to the waiting scientists. To some, the message was relayed by telephone. In certain cases, CAP mobile radio cars were assigned to take the traffic and hand-carry it to the Moonwatch or camera stations which, as we have seen, are usually located in isolated or outlying areas. In other instances, CAP set up portable communications stations right at the observation site. Camera stations got their photos, thanks to the orbital predictions sent to them by radio.

But we are ahead of our story. Long before Sputnik I was launched—in fact, nearly a year before—the CAP was involved in another aspect of Moonwatch—the actual training of the volunteers. Since no satellite had yet been launched, Moonwatchers faced the same problems as did Minitrack—that is, how do you know if you will be ready when the time arrives? Minitrack could use the signals that the Army obligingly bounced off the moon but Moonwatch was a visual thing. Was it possible that a satellite could be simulated with the use of airplanes?

The CAP said "Certainly. It would really be very simple."

The device they chose was, believe it or not, the familiar household tool known as the plumber's helper. Attached to the suction end was a common ordinary flashlight lamp—two-dollars' worth of parts you could purchase at any hardware store. When that strange and unglamorous device, endearingly called "the bug," was towed through the night skies behind a CAP plane, it appeared almost like a real satellite hundreds of miles above the earth. All across the country, the volunteer CAP crews began flying training missions for the volunteers of Project Moonwatch. In more than a hundred isolated locations throughout the country these individual "dry runs" took place. Sometimes they were not so "dry."

Mike Harloff, now with NASA, was at that time attached to Project Vanguard, while volunteering time with CAP. He recalls that on one drizzly evening a local Washington, D.C., area team was getting ready for a CAP "flyby." "Because of the poor visibility, I was to stand down there with the Moonwatch team and signal to the pilot with a flashlight so he'd know where we were. Well, he came by all right, but kept right on going. About twenty minutes later he returned and we had our practice run. After the pilot landed I asked him what happened—why he'd disappeared for twenty minutes. It turned out he'd been following the light of a locomotive as it moved down the track towards Richmond."

There comes a time when all the separate components must be welded into one team, or functioning network. And it was anybody's guess as to the results of the December 8, 1956 first national Moonwatch alert. How would these widely scattered, volunteer amateur astronomers perform as a unit?

The alert was to be carried out by every station, regardless of weather conditions. They were to commence observing fifteen minutes after sunset and continue for almost two hours. The stations were advised that there might be a simulated satellite flyby in their area, but in any event, all station leaders were to make a report to headquarters, even if only a negative one.

The results of this alert were gratifying, and although there were a number of problems with communications, time signals, and even eyestrain on the part of the observers, it was considered successful. With practice and some minor changes in operating procedures, Moonwatch would be ready to meet the challenge when it came.

Another practice alert was held during the evening twilight of July 19, 1957, and eighty Moonwatch teams participated, with CAP providing flybys. The exercise showed a marked improvement over the previous alert.

It wasn't long before the Russians provided the Moonwatch teams around the world with an object to track far more spectacular than a plumber's helper. The Terre Haute, Indiana, team was the first to report an observation of Sputnik I, on October 6, 1957. The observation was questionable and the first confirmed observations were made on October 8 by the Moonwatch stations in Sidney and Woomera, Australia. The New Haven, Connecticut, team was the first in the United States to obtain a confirmed observation.

Meanwhile, the teams were getting a bit of unexpected help in the form of a satellite simulator developed under contract with Mr. Jack A. Wagener of Gloucester, New Jersey. Also, the National Geographical Society designed a map and overlay kit to aid observers in making their satellite predictions.

Those were exciting and wonderful days for a world preparing to enter the new space age. They were the days of make-do, of experiments and inventiveness, and for many young people it was a time when their careers were channeled irrevocably towards the heavens. Parents and teachers answered the call of the young for leadership and guidance, often at great personal sacrifice, for these activities were always extracurricular. It was mother who got up in the middle of the night to fix breakfast for her young Moonwatcher so he could be at his post at four A.M., and Dad had to somehow get him there, often in the cold and snow. Teachers gave up their Saturdays to work with scientific clubs. They would go home from an evening of observing with their team, spend half the night correcting classroom papers and appear at the station again for a dawn pass.

Those were exciting and wonderful days for a world preparing to enter the new space age. Parents and teachers answered the call of the young for leadership and guidance.

An example of one distinguished Moonwatch team could be found at Wakefield High School in Arlington, Virginia. Science teacher David Saltus, who was the team's faculty sponsor, explains their background. "We started out as a rocket society. My reason for sponsoring it was that I felt we needed high quality scientists in this country. The enthusiasm that generates and sustains the quality scientist is often born in high school. Also, I was convinced from experience that rocketry is a field with great educational value. Many skills and techniques are involved in constructing and firing even the simplest rockets."

Saltus shakes his head and smiles as he reminisces. "The first year we attempted to fire four rockets from the safest place I knew—the banks of the Potomac river. Well, the rockets all exploded and the police came to investigate. At the time, the experience did not seem valuable, what with an irate policeman muttering about bringing explosives onto Government property and the later newspaper item, "Rocketeering Students Jolt Earth Police." But it taught me, that each rocket-club sponsor ought to be technically competent. Our rockets exploded because some misguided soul thought that a little potassium chlorate would add zip to zinc and sulphur fuel. Well, after that, we made up a list of ground rules."

Along with ground rules, the young rocketeers enlisted the aid of an Army missile expert at Fort Belvoir, Virginia, Lt. Colonel Charles M. Parkin. Colonel Parkin first got approval from the Department of Defense to conduct a test program to assist teen-age rocketeers. Then he took them on a tour of missile facilities, instructed them in the safe handling of rockets and propellants and ran a series of Army supervised launchings. The Pentagon was so impressed with the success of the Wakefield group that it gave the green light to a nationwide program of Army assistance to the teen-age rocket movement. In all, five thousand young missile men responded.

The Rocketeer Club of Wakefield High was a natural for Moonwatch. Before long, students, bundled up in heavy coats and blankets, were manning the scopes on the school's rooftops during the cold winter evenings and chilly dawns. Needing money for equipment, they decided to go into the Tastee Doughnut business. Much to the school's alarm, customers were weaned away from the cafeteria in droves, but before the Moonwatch team gave up its profitable sales campaign, there was enough money to buy a really good telescope to present to Wakefield High School.

To pass away the time during the nocturnal vigils, students listened to music from the all-night radio station WTOP. But at dawn, when the stars suddenly dimmed, a kind of poetic hush would come over the junior scientists. Saltus remembers one tall lad murmuring more to himself than to anybody else, "Apollo sending his golden shafts to shoot down the stars."

There were moments of excitement, too, such as the sighting of a flash of light traveling slowly on the horizon. "The boys nearly jumped off the roof!" It wasn't Sputnik after all; only a jet.

The Wakefield team has some thrilling memories for its scrapbook. Imagine having *the* director of Project Vanguard, Dr. John P. Hagen, manning the scope right alongside you! The reason of course was that Dr. Hagen's son, Peter, was the team's assistant leader. (Peter is now taking graduate work in astronomy.) And then there was the telegram from President Eisenhower, dated 1 February 1958, which congratulated the Wakefield High Moonwatch team on its contribution to the project. As of December 31, 1957, the team had made three of the twenty-one observations from stations in their area.

Inventiveness was encouraged, and competition was keen for practical, workable ideas. Bill Murdaugh, son of Admiral and Mrs. A. C. Murdaugh, won $200 for his "satellite tracer," in a competition sponsored jointly by Atlantic Research Corporation of Alexandria, Virginia and WTOP-TV. He explains how he got the idea: "I was lying in bed one night looking out the window. I watched a plane go by and I though how easy it was to trace its course through the glass so I jumped up and got a piece of soap and mapped it out right there. The plane was flying very slowly. My folks thought I was crazy." Bill's satellite tracer, a pane of glass mounted on a stand, was promptly placed on the roof of the school for further testing.

Moonwatch played cupid in a number of cases. When the Baltimore team announced the engagement of two of its members, Miss Margaret Tiemann and Mr. Harry Larkins, Jr., it was learned that they made their happy decision on the evening of February 1, 1958 when they had adjacent telescopes and shared the same foot-warming blanket.

Oh yes, there were girls. They called themselves GAMS (Girls' Auxiliary Moonwatch Society).

Elsewhere in the United States, the Cincinnati Moonwatch team, under Thomas Van Flandern, organized a local network of teams designed primarily to share Cincinnati's use of an IBM 7090 on which the teams employed a culmination satellite prediction program—predicting when the satellite would die.

Moonwatchers everywhere were proud of the job they were doing. There was a great feeling of comraderie among the specialized groups. A New Orleans, Louisiana, team designed a four-inch, circular, blue and gold arm-patch for their observing jackets. The patch, with a satellite appliqued in the center, had the words "Operation Moonwatch" above, and "Official Satellite Tracker" below. The Bloemfontein Moonwatch team spread their motto around the world: "If at first you don't succeed, keep peeping!" The Arizona Moonwatch team gave up their group leader, Hal Cozzens, when he was selected as a member of the Baker-Nunn team, as were some of the other Moonwatchers.

In Madison, Wisconsin, team leader Margaret Frish constructed a precise drum-type timing machine which was capable of reading to .01 seconds. A single pen traversed the rotating drum by way of a screw movement. Separate observers "signed" their fixes with individual dot-dash signatures. Thirty-five minutes worth of observations could be recorded on a single 8½ by 11-inch sheet.

At the Pan American College Observatory, Edinburg, Texas, Paul Engle decided that Moonwatchers deserved special attention because some of the students who participated in Moonwatch were "among the most outstanding young people in science." He established annual meetings of the astronomical and astronautic institute for boys and girls in the upper three classes of high school. The first part of the six-week session was concerned with introducing the student to astronomy and astrophysics; the second, to astronautics and space technology. Enrollment was limited to thirty-two.

During their heyday, Moonwatch teams around the world turned in an extremely impressive record. Between 1957 and December of 1960, the volunteers reported the very first observations on no fewer than 17 satellites of the 68 objects known to have been in orbit. In other words, Moonwatch acquired twenty-five percent of all objects in orbit, and a far higher proportion of the objects for which the SAO had been responsible. In addition Moonwatchers relocated three satellites after they had been lost by other tracking systems. They were 1958 ALPHA, 1958 EPSILON (they found it twice), and 1959 DELTA II. Vanguard II, in 1959, was feared lost beyond recall and many were skeptical that even Moonwatch could find it. Alex Geddes of SAO, after days of work, fitted selected observations of unidentified objects into a pattern which seemed to fit an orbit. Then astronomer Jack Slowey took these pieces and proved they did fit and the rocket was reacquired.

Since the beginning of the program in 1956, approximately 265 teams had been registered, with a total membership of 8,000.

Moonwatch became a part of the community, the nation, and the world. If anything moved in the sky, Moonwatch tracked it. As an example of their alertness, on May 31, 1961, team leader Dr. John B. Allen of Dallas reported a sighting of a freshly fallen meteorite. These are of great interest to researchers because they contain short-life radioactive isotopes that rapidly disappear. These isotopes are produced by cosmic rays in space and are our most important source of information concerning rays in the distant regions of space. The 18-pound 7-ounce meteorite which impacted on the night of May 30 was quickly turned over to the Smithsonian for analysis. Five other laboratories across the country, and the National Museum, also received pieces of the find, thanks to Moonwatch.

Moonwatch served in many capacities, including back-up missions such as that for Project Echo—1960 IOTA I. This was a 100-foot-diameter inflatable polyester-foam sphere, coated with aluminum and used as a reflector for a series of passive communications-satellite experiments. It was placed into a near-circular, 1,000-mile orbit by a DELTA III stage rocket. Moonwatch was alerted to track this object in case of failure of the two waferlike tracking beacons which were attached to opposite sides of the sphere. The transmitter did continue to work so that Minitrack could follow its travels.

However, Moonwatch came into its own on the next phase. Due to the fact that sunlight plays an important part in maintaining the sphere's shape, it was possible that it would partially deflate as it entered the earth shadow. The thirty pounds of sublimating material, which provides inflation, turns into gas at temperatures slightly above freezing. In continuous sunlight, the temperature of the satellite averages about 239 degrees; in shadow, it rapidly drops to well below freezing. Therefore, once out of the sunlight, gases used to keep the satellite inflated will return to a solid state. It was very important that scientists learn precisely what would happen to the satellite as it entered into shadow and reentered into sunlight. Moonwatch observations provided the necessary information.

We noted that Moonwatchers seemed to be everywhere on the globe. There were even two special-status Moonwatch stations set up on ice islands that were floating in the Arctic. New London, Connecticut, Moonwatchers Dr. Robert H. Mellen and Dr. Elton P. Kelley set up their vigils on Islands T-3 and Charlie. These men were on a scientfiic expedition for the U.S. Navy (acoustics research) and carried on their Moonwatching as an off-duty hobby. Their observations were particularly useful because of their position near the North Pole. Such observations were reported by radio with telegraphic relays from Peru, Indiana.

Moonwatch continued to provide valuable data, even after the IGY officially ended in 1959. Its shape has changed, and the original 225 teams have been reduced to half that number. The Moonwatch program now consists of 12 "precision," 22 "standard," and 121 "limited" teams and independent affiliates.

Observing techniques have been vastly improved and instrumentation has been upgraded. Most teams now use telescopes capable of 21 x 120 magnification, as contrasted with the original 7 x 50's. Accuracy of time in 1957 was slightly less than one second of time and one degree of arc; today Moonwatch, under the leadership of Richard C. Vanderburgh, a former airlines pilot, claims an accuracy approaching a tenth of a second of time and six minutes of arc. A real achievement!

With the establishment of today's sophisticated tracking systems, Moonwatch is no longer vitally important in finding, or searching for, satellites. It now directs its talents toward the recording and reporting of special visual characteristics and the observing of entering and reentering objects. Visual characteristics observers will continue on the basis of specific requests for magnitude and tumbling estimates (the brightness of the object and how fast it is tumbling). Moonwatchers will also describe what they see as rocket stages separate in flight and the satellite performs its precalibrated maneuvers. The successful observation of entering objects (meteorites), while of very significant scientific value, is still a matter of remote chance. Reentry observing (decaying satellites) has advanced from random sighting to coordinated and predictable reentry patrols for quick recovery of objects impacting the earth.

Moonwatchers around the world—students, teachers, professional astronomers—citizens all, deserve a hearty "well done!" as the Navy would say. The chapters they wrote in the annals of the sky rangers' history will not be forgotten.

9

Tracking for Defense

The greater the power to detect
The greater is the power to protect.

IN the shadow of Colorado's Rampart Range, in the city of Colorado Springs, lies Ent Air Force Base, home of Headquarters, North American Air Defense Command (NORAD). The setting is magnificent, yet somehow disturbing when you think of the grim tasks NORAD may have to perform. Here in the sparkling sunshine in "God's country," prehistoric mountains and sienna-colored rock formations are silhouetted against the sky as ghostly reminders of the past. Pikes Peak pokes its cap of white through the soft cloud, while below, primeval pine forests shelter deer, elk, and mountain lion. The air at this altitude is like champagne; the breezes are fresh and usually quite brisk. You feel healthy and clear-headed and awed by the splendor of the giant artwork etched into the red mountain, appropriately call the "Garden of the Gods." It is so peaceful . . . so grand. You want it to remain that way.

As you ponder this thought, it somehow makes sense to have a mighty military center situated here for it is NORAD's job "to defend the North American Continent against aerospace attack."

Notice we say North American Continent. Because our continent is so vast, Canada and the United States recognized their mutual problems of defense, and in September of 1957 agreed that a cooperative plan of action was the most feasible.

Both countries now operate under a single command responsible to the two governments. Commander in chief is four-star General Dean Strother, USAF; and Deputy Commander in chief is Air Marshal C. R. Dunlap, RCAF. Both of them are on full-time assignment to NORAD.

In the weapons field the RCAF Air Defense Command (RCAF ADC) provides fighter interceptor squadrons equipped with CF-101B "Voodoo" aircraft and two surface-to-air Bomarc missile squadrons. They also contribute heavily in the area of surveillance and in the detection and identification functions.

The commanders of the NORAD component commands also serve as principal advisors to the Commander in chief of NORAD on matters pertaining to the services they represent.

The Alaskan Command is a United States unified command with a twofold mission. The first is the ground defense of the State of Alaska, and the second part is air defense. For that section of his mission which deals with air defense, the Commander in chief of the Alaskan Command is responsible to CINCNORAD. Thus, all the forces engaged in the aerospace defense of North America are under the operational control of a single commander. This is quite a responsibility when you ponder it.

In NORAD's potpourri of military brass you never know whom you will see working side by side, marching smartly

North American Air Defense Command is a joint program of the United States and Canada to provide air and space defense against hostile attacks. Several systems and networks are utilized, including the RCAF's Baker-Nunn cameras. This particular electronically controlled camera which produces highly accurate film records of objects in space—up to 100,000 miles—is located at Primrose Lake, Alberta.

down the halls, or lunching together at the club. Traditional service rivalries seem to be temporarily shelved as Army, Navy, USAF, RCAF, and even Marines, find themselves as members of one big NORAD family. It is intriguing to see so many second lieutenants, who were once nearly extinct. This new breed of shavetails does not consist of jet jockeys or airplane drivers, because aerospace defense calls for scientists and technicians trained in the fields of astronomy, astrophysics and celestial mathematics.

At the opposite end of the pole, there is no place outside the Pentagon with such a heavy concentration of power. The last count netted a star-studded cast of twenty-nine generals, including all of those assigned to NORAD, ADC, and ARADCOM.

Since NORAD's mission is defense, there must be some warning of hostile attack through a worldwide system of radar, radio, and optical sensors. There are three basic categories in this mammoth network; one for bomber aircraft, one for missiles, and one for space objects.

In the first category, to warn of approaching bombers we have the Pinetree system across southern Canada, the mid-Canada line, and the DEW (Distant Early Warning) line, which stretches all the way from the western end of the Aleutian Islands to the east coast of Greenland. Airborne extensions of the DEW line—from the Aleutians to Midway Island on the west, and from the east coast of Greenland to the British Islands on the east—are flown by radar-equipped planes of the U.S. Navy. Should a sneak attack be attempted, our aircraft would immediately be sent to intercept them.

But what about unmanned bombers . . . missiles?

It is well known that missiles can travel thousands of miles at tremendous speeds so that no spot on earth is free of their threat. A special system of detecting missiles is needed. There are now three BMEWS (Ballistic Missile Early Warning System) sites in operation which represent the completed system: Thule, Greenland; Clear, Alaska; and Fylingdales Moor, England. Should an alarm come from these stations, anti-missile missiles such as Nike-Zeus would be sent to intercept the attackers.

The third defense area—space objects—is, at present, restricted to surveillance, detection, and identification. Ideally, we should have the capability of intercepting a satellite for inspection. Should it prove to have hostile intent, we should then destroy it. Just how far we have progressed in these areas is classified information, but by pure conjecture and a bit of digging around we learn that steps are being taken in this area. These steps we will explore in greater detail as we acquaint ourselves with the military tracking picture. We can guess at the moment that one day sky rangers will move from earth-based to space-based facilities. With sophistication of space vehicles, manned space-platforms will provide guidance and even hangaring of space interceptors.

In the meantime, as Bob Hope described our military

The present Combat Operations Center at Headquarters NORAD near Colorado Springs is unprotected from thermonuclear attack, but by 1965, the entire center will be moved into a gigantic three-story structure which has been blasted out of the heart of nearby Cheyenne Mountain.

The $88.7 million "hardened" site will be accessible by a one-mile tunnel from the north and from the south.

trackers in remote areas he was visiting, "These boys are playing a wonderful new game out here. It's called Lots of Luck."

And on the bookcase in the information office at NORAD is a battered bugle, made in Canada. It was explained, "If all else fails, we'll use that to blow retreat."

This kind of puckishness is a healthy relief from the awe-inspiring undercurrent of serious concern, twenty-four hours a day, seven days a week. "You work with what you have at hand and you hope that the wrong people don't discover the infrequent gaps," is the general feeling. A sense of humor can help immensely as a kind of relief valve. The military has always had this. "In house" jokes, slapstick cartoons where the CO takes the brunt, or goofy diplomas for those who have had the course all add to morale and cement the family together. And the military at NORAD deserve every small chuckle they can get.

Nerve center of NORAD is the Combat Operations Center (COC) situated in a two-story concrete, windowless blockhouse. It is from this center that first warnings of attack on this continent would come, and if such an attack should come it is from this center that the air battle for survival of the United States and Canada would be directed. At present, COC is unprotected from thermonuclear attack, but during 1965 the entire center will be moved into a gigantic three-story structure which has been blasted out of the heart of nearby Cheyenne Mountain. The $88.7 million "Hardened" site will be accessible by a one-mile tunnel from the north and from the south.

Here at the Combat Operations Center, data is received and stored in a large digital computer from the huge complex of radar stations, interceptor squadrons, missile sites, space-tracking and ballistic-missile warning units, and the regions and sectors that make up NORAD. Pertinent information concerning the air defense of North America or concerning warning of impending attack is electronically displayed by a system known as ICONORAMA.

ICONORAMA permits almost instantaneous observation of the positions of aerospace and seaborne objects thousands of miles away, and over any part of the continent covered by radar networks.

It is an eerie, uncomfortable feeling to walk into the darkened theater and see what amounts to the most gigantic sky spy system ever devised by man, at least on this continent. (The Soviets are thought to have many more tracking stations than we.) No Hollywood thriller can compare to the real drama of observing distant aerospace and seaborne objects spread out on the cinerama-type screen.

The main screen, 24 by 32 feet, is used for keeping track of "air-breathing" aircraft. The screen is black with an outlined map of North America, the surrounding islands, Greenland, Iceland, and parts of Siberia and the Carribean islands. Symbols show the location and direction of travel of all aircraft of special interest. We learn that identified hostile air-breathing objects show up in red, while unknowns are flashed in orange.

To the left of the air-breathing screen is the smaller BMEWS one. At its top is an ominous threat-summary panel which provides the number of missiles predicted to impact on North America and the estimated time they will impact. The lower part of the BMEWS display is a map of Europe and Asia as seen looking over the North Pole from North America.

To the right of the main display is the weapons-status board. There is a commander's box score which shows the number of hostile aircraft in the NORAD system, the number of unknowns, the weapons committed to these tracks, the kills made, and NORAD losses. Below this is a listing of the major military commands, worldwide, and their defense readiness conditions. The bottom part of the status board shows the number of weapons available to NORAD on five-minute alert—fighter interceptors and surface-to-air missiles.

As we watch the screen, we see a Russian aircraft en route from Havana to Moscow. Elsewhere we see Soviet trawlers, a SAC mission, or a tracking mission in operation. Major Glenn Perryman, Director of Central Computor and Display Facility (CCandDF) explains that we have "real time"

It is an eerie, uncomfortable feeling to walk into the darkened theater at COC and see what amounts to the most gigantic sky spy system ever devised by man, at least on this continent. ICONORAMA permits almost instantaneous observation of the positions of aerospace and seaborne objects thousands of miles away.

information (real time meaning *as it happens*) for the Commander in chief and battle staff. The atmosphere in the COC is businesslike, with conversation centered around the consoles, the square switches which are lighted up in green (all systems operating), orange (partially incapacitated), or red (temporarily out). All but two or three buttons are green and we are assured that all back-up systems are operational. This is a comfort, especially when

Major Perryman suggests we might like to experience a real test alert.

What would happen in this very room should a warning come through from any part of the network? The way to find out is by going into a "test mode." This is done by running a test tape through the computer which controls the BMEWS display. The tape feeds impulses (approximately like those which would occur during an ICBM attack) through the computer and thence to the display equipment.

Suddenly lighted numbers begin flickering as if something had gotten into the machines and made them go berserk! An unseen hand begins circling areas on screens—"ellipses of impact." It is calmly explained that here is where the weapons will strike. In this case, the zones are Los Angeles, Detroit, Washington, and Colorado Springs. The time of impact is flashed for each city. You shudder at the coldly precise manner in which this life-and-death game of chess is being played.

The "game" is over in a few minutes, but even during the test mode, had a real alarm been reported, the screen would have been automatically wiped clean and replaced by the true alarm information.

Communications at COC are nothing short of fantastic when you realize the vast distances involved. Major Perryman picks up a phone and punches a button. He is immediately talking with Major MacWilliams in Fylingdales Moor in England. Would we like to chat a bit with the newest BMEWS site?

Of course. Major MacWilliams' voice is as clear as if he were in the next room.

After saying good-bye (cheerio) to England, we call Clear, Alaska, which is located just outside of Fairbanks. Again, the voice comes through perfectly. We learn that the earthquake has not damaged the BMEWS site too badly, although there are cracks in the walls and other minor problems with the buildings. (General Gerhart, former commander of NORAD, later announced that Clear was "out" for seven minutes during the quake. This was not serious, however, because the enemy would have had to know exactly when the quake would strike in order to take advantage of our blind spot.)

Talking with the BMEWS people in Thule, Greenland, we find that a Russian trawler has again cut through our communications cable so we resort to a tropo-scatter technique of radio communication. Major Perryman explains this back-up system: "Here, you take the energy from the voice and shoot it up until it hits the ceiling of the troposphere. It picks up energy and is reamplified."

SPADATS

Now that we have been introduced to the NORAD family of warning facilities and stumbled through the mass of anagram names, we bring one member of the family into focus. It is called SPADATS—Space Detection and Tracking System.

SPADATS does not operate sensors, but is the center into which data from all over the world pour. Through a global system of radar, radio, and optical sensors, SPADATS detects, tracks, and catalogs *all* man-made objects and provides the decision makers at NORAD with up-to-the-minute space-tracking data.

Giant digital computers make mathematical computations at the rate of 160,000 additions or subtractions per second, and 50,000 multiplications or divisions per second. A memory core capable of storing over 32,000 words provides split-second printed answers at more than 21,000 words per minute. Once the computers have digested all the tracking data and produced their findings, the information is displayed on large status boards in the SPADATS operations-control center. From here it is piped into the battle-staff area in the adjacent combat operations center via closed-circuit television.

In case of a breakdown or malfunction of the complicated computing systems, there is a back-up group of "brains" at Hanscom Field, Bedford, Massachusetts.

If *that* breaks down, our attention is directed toward the ancient, tried-and-true object hanging on the wall: an abacus.

10

Spacetrack

T HE primary contributor to the SPADATS operation is the United States Air Force. The USAF Spacetrack
system, under the command of Air Defense Command's 9th
Aerospace Defense Division is responsible for the largest
portion of the operation, and it is the "Ninth Aero" which
operates the SPADATS center for NORAD. This is the
world's first full-time aerospace defense organization. Its
mission is twofold: first, alerting the free world of a missile
or satellite launched attack (BMEWS); and second, to receive, process, and catalog data on all man-made objects in
space.

When we say *all* man-made objects we are referring to the
count of June, 1965, of 581—most of which is "junk." Although the number continually varies, 150 satellites are
payload, which means that they are scientifically equipped
packages; 124 were launched by the United States, 22 by
the Russians, 2 by the United Kingdom, 1 by Canada, and
1 by Italy. And then there are the 391 pieces of junk!

There is a lot of junk in space and it is a miserable job to keep track of it as it whirls around in all shapes and sizes. The junk is the result of explosions which may cause one satellite to become fifty. Nose cones, debris, pieces of equipment no larger than a pencil or teacup, come zinging through the radar screens, silently, steadily, day after day. Sometimes a piece will come through sideways, but on the next orbit, it will be flattened. Payloads, burned-out boosters, wires, nuts and bolts—all must be accounted for.

Junk is identified by its orbital behavior. You know that this is a piece of such-and-such satellite which was launched on a certain date. Unfortunately, the junk's orbital behavior changes in the same manner as does the lively satellite. Atmospheric drag, solar rays, and the earth's oblate shape affect the nuts and bolts so that their orbits must be constantly updated. The Ninth Aero must keep up their routine of constant predict-look-predict-refine for the life of every piece of stuff that is up there.

The task is an enormous one, considering the fact that in July of 1961, when the Ninth was born, the Spacetrack Center was receiving and processing about 12,000 observations per month from 33 objects in orbit. Today, the Center averages one observation received and processed every twelve seconds, around the clock, seven days a week. It is estimated that by 1970 there will be some 7,000 man-made objects orbiting this planet—quite a chore for our blue-suited sky rangers!

How does the system work?

Each time an observation is made by one of their field sensors, the data is transmitted by high speed communications to the Spacetrack Center at Colorado Springs. Here, the data is fed into the computer facility which tells them of the orbital trajectory (is it eccentric or stable?). An analysis is made as to the decay rate or new motions of the vehicle,

BALLISTIC MISSILE EARLY WARNING SYSTEM

SITE I

SITE II

SITE III

SITE II
CLEAR
ALASKA

SITE I
THULE
GREENLAND

SITE III
FYLINGDALES MOOR
ENGLAND

NORAD

SAC

PENTAGON

...MBAT OPERATIONS CENTER

REARWARD COMMUNICATIONS

and there follows a determination of the vehicle's mission. Is it scientific or military? Friendly or hostile? And finally, the experts predict its future behavior; positioning it in space and figuring look-angles for retransmission to their units in the field.

The Spacetrack Center at Colorado Springs has upwards of 1,500 sources of information; their own units consist of

BMEWS Sites I, II, and III, and others which are pure satellite sensors. They are located at Shemya, Alaska; Moorestown, New Jersey; Eglin AFB, Florida; and Cloudcroft, New Mexico. Other contributors are the Air Force Systems Command (AFSC), Baker-Nunn cameras in Turkey, Oslo, Norway, Edwards AFB, and Patrick Air Force Base's network of sensors, particularly Trinidad Island.

The Navy's Space Surveillance System (of which we shall hear shortly), with its curtain across the southern United

Across the top of the world from the peaceful English countryside at Fylingdales Moor, to Thule, Greenland, to Clear, Alaska, lie the three great Ballistic Missile Early Warning Sites. Shown here is Clear, Alaska.

The men of BMEWS live like moles in underground tunnels, dwarfed by the enormity of the instruments they keep. They are trained technicians, technological specialists whose erudition far surpasses their youthful appearance, masters of mathematics, cosmic explorers on the alert—all of them sensitive to the heartbeat and pulse of their charge.

States, sends its data to the Center. Also in the network are the Atlantic and Pacific Missile Range Complexes.

Data is received from about 600 additional sensors located around the world. The majority of these others belong to the civilian scientific community and to educational institutions. Among them are the Smithsonian Astrophysical Observatory with its twelve Baker-Nunn cameras; NASA's Minitrack stations; M.I.T.; the University of South Africa;

and the powerful telescopes of Mount Palomar, California, Schenectady, New York, and Evanston, Illinois.

Through worldwide communications facilities of AIR-COMNET (Air Communications Network), Spacetrack provides satellite activity data on a continuous basis to Strategic Air Command, the White Sands Proving Ground, and other military and government agencies. Satellite information is also made available to NASA—and to the world, via the United Nations.

The "eyes and ears" of Spacetrack consist of a variety of equipment, placed in what seem to be outlandish areas of the earth's surface. Awesome, incongruous with the countryside which is quiet and primitive as in the days of old, they somehow seem unreal. This is particularly true of BMEWS.

BMEWS

Across the top of the world, from the peaceful English countryside at Fylingdales Moor, to Thule, Greenland, to Clear, Alaska, lie the three great Ballistic Missile Early Warning Sites, shooting their beams thousands of miles out into space. The chain of strange structures silhouetted against the cold skies loom separately, yet are invisibly linked to one another as watchtowers of the free world—probing, penetrating, reaching out into space from the top of the world. It is a fantasy land of reality, set within a science-fiction atmosphere of what could be another planet.

Transmitters, platforms, klystron towers, and wave guides stretch out for miles overhead, transmitting energy which is driving through the huge arteries . . . pulsing the life-giving plasma of radar energy to the man-made monster that has long since dwarfed its creator, yet serves him faithfully.

They are not unlike a giant pipe-organ whose surge of concertos and sensitized chords are concentrated to form a tremendous sounding board for the lanes of infinity.

Shown here is a youthful British sky ranger inside computer room at Fylingdales Moor BMEWS site.

Men of BMEWS live like moles in underground tunnels, dwarfed by the enormity of the instruments they keep. Trained technicians, technological specialists whose erudition far surpasses their youthful appearance, masters of mathematics, cosmic explorers on the alert, sensitive to the heartbeat and pulse of their charge, listen and watch as their giant scanner reaches out to grab invisible signals from the highway of the universe. They have long since become accustomed to having one foot on earth and the other in the stars. Their gigantic equipment makes them a part of the heavens.

There are two types of radar which our BMEWS sky rangers employ to detect and track possible ballistic missile attack and satellites. There are fixed fan radars, graphically called "football fields" which measure over 400 feet in length and 165 feet in height. (In size they are equivalent to a forty-story building tipped over on its side, nestled in snow.) The great steel parabolas can reach over 2,000 miles into space. When an object moves over them, they get a "hit" on their

"Football fields" (General Electric AN/FPS-50) used at Clear, Alaska, and Thule, Greenland, are built to withstand wind velocities up to 180 knots and can operate even with a six-inch coating of ice.

The RCA AN/FPS-49 can both scan and track. The protective dome is made of 1,700 hectagonal panels of laminated fiber glass with honeycombed paper sandwiched between. It is capable of range detection out to 40 million miles. Shown here are the radomes at Site III, Fylingdales Moor, England.

screens. These detection radars, combined with computers, provide information on the probable launch area, impact area, time of impact and so on.

These "football fields" (General Electric AN/FPS-50) used at Clear, Alaska, and Thule, Greenland, are built to withstand wind velocities up to 180 knots and operate even with a six-inch coating of ice. There are two sets of beams, one above the other, which fan over a given sector. Should a missile penetrate the lower fan, it would trigger the alarm, announcing that an attack was under way. The upper fan provides information about the intruder's trajectory, speed, probable launch point, general impact area and impact time. This is true not only in the case of a single missile, but large numbers of missiles in the event of a mass attack.

The second type of radar is the RCA AN/FPS-49 which can both scan and track. The "49" resembles an enormous white bubble or golf ball, for its 84-foot dish is housed inside a 140-foot radome. This protective dome is made of 1,700 hectagonal panels of laminated fiberglass with honeycombed paper sandwiched between. The rotating "49" is flexible in that it can be assigned to scan over various sectors at different elevation angles. Upon detection of a target, the 55-ton tracking radar "locks on" and follows it. Accurate to plus-or-minus 0.00001 second of arc, it is capable of range detection out to approximately 40 million miles! The dish inside the radome is powerful enough to track an object one meter square at a range of 2,000 miles.

The ideal arrangement, such as at Thule, is to have a combination of the two radar systems: the fixed fan to find the object, and the tracker with its powerful narrow beam to follow it.

At each site where these radar systems have been placed, there is a pair of solid-state computers. This duplication of the computers permits one to take over the functions of another during either scheduled or unscheduled shutdowns for maintenance, thus assuring continuous operation. The functions of these computers is to compute target trajectories from digitized target information, to compare the trajectories with (1) observed satellites, (2) the characteristics of the rising light of morning dawn, and (3) the characteristics of meteor trails, so that mistaken identification will be prevented. In the case of numerous targets, they decide which tracking radars should cover selected targets. This

View from inside the 140-foot protective radome of the "49" shows the 55-ton tracking radar which can "lock on" to a target and follow it.

information is then transmitted to NORAD for display on the panel. The Commander in chief, NORAD, makes the final decision as to whether or not this is an attack.

This, then, is BMEWS, supplier of seventy percent of SPADATS' useful defense information on what is going on in space. And again, as with Minitrack and SAO, we find the kaleidoscope of color and contrast. Again, there is the pioneering spirit which takes men (and in the case of Clear,

Alaska, the contract employees' families, too) into the rugged wildernesses of earth so that the mysteries of outer space may be unveiled. At the same time they are assuring us that our safety from space aggression is their prime concern.

Who, for instance, would voluntarily trek to Thule, Greenland, far to the north of the Arctic Circle, where the most direct aerial route from Soviet Russia is centered? Certainly no one except the most highly motivated of the tracking experts. This site, the first in the chain, is nearly as close to Moscow as it is to Seattle and New York; yet here our sky

The BMEWS site at Thule, Greenland, has the ideal arrangement of "football field" radars to find the object in space and radomes to follow it. Thule, a name which stems from *Ultima Thule*, means "utmost end." The Eskimo village has been moved to the north but natives still visit the sky rangers at the BMEWS site.

rangers reside and work in the snow and cold of the wilderness twelve miles outside of Thule Air Force Base.

Even the name itself, "Ultima Thule," given it by the Danish explorer Knud Rasmussen, means "the utmost end," or the farthest possible limit man could travel.

Strangely enough, even though the original Eskimo village has been moved sixty miles to the north, Thule is not a lonely life for our sky rangers. There are, at the complex, nearly 6,000 personnel, including Air Force, Army, and Danish civilians, plus seventeen Coast Guardsmen located at Cape Atholl, a remote weather station thirty miles away. Many of the old Eskimo sod houses, including Knud Rasmussen's, still stand and are in usable condition, even though the space age has brought $400 million in BMEWS equipment, alone, to its snowy shores. Operated by 642 RCA civilians, 13 Air Force officers, and 36 airmen of the 71st Surveillance Wing, the Thule site is tremendously important to our aerospace defense system.

Although the climate is not nearly so severe as many imagine, temperatures can slip to 43 degrees below zero in wintertime. Ships can usually get into the harbor about the 10th of July but all vessels must leave by the 15th of October, or risk being frozen in. Both Thule and its sister site, Clear, Alaska, are completely self-sufficient bases with all necessary facilities to support the administrative, operating, and maintenance personnel stationed at each base. BMEWS arctic bases are designed to be thriving small cities, complete with comfortable living quarters (two or three men to a room), good meals, medical facilities, and a variety of recreational outlets such as a gymnasium, hobby shops, bowling alley, movies, TV, and sports in season. This all sounds quite ordinary until we look a bit further.

What about transportation?

In the summer, light planes and helicopters are used, but

in the winter, sky rangers turn to the "Pole Cat," or tractor train, to get around in. The Pole Cat is a small tracked vehicle, completely enclosed, with heater, radio, and food supply. It usually pulls one or two trailer sleds, the insides of which look like an airliner with eight airplane-type seats, a heater, radio equipment, and fuel supply. The Pole Cat is used only to carry passengers and mail.

The other larger train, much less plush, is called the "Big Swing." The tractor is a large special Caterpillar, called the "Sno-Cat." Its tracks are over three feet wide and it, too, is completely enclosed, heated, and radio-equipped. It usually pulls from four to eight trailer sleds, each almost as large as a railroad boxcar. A typical train would consist of a sleeper-trailer with bunks for 25 people; a kitchen-mess-hall trailer; a radio-navigation trailer; and an electrical-power trailer to supply heat and power for the entire train.

While the plush Pole Cat zings along at about ten miles per hour, the Big Swing creeps at about one-half mile per hour in the dangerous crevasse areas at the edge of the ice cap. Once past that, it goes full speed ahead at three miles per hour!

Many sky rangers remember better days when they jogged along steamy corduroy roads in pickup trucks or buses to station sites in the south. But here at Thule, they watch through the Big Swing's windows as it maneuvers across the treacherous ice cap. The trail is marked with red flags on poles about eight feet tall, spaced about 100 yards apart. Every fifth pole is of metal so that it can be seen by the radar in the navigation trailer. The other poles are made of bamboo. The trains keep moving so long as they can see the next flag ahead, either visually or by radar. When they cannot see the next flag, they stop and wait—maybe two or three days—until they can see it. The reason for the poor visibility is that whenever the wind exceeds twenty or twenty-five miles per hour, the air is full of blowing snow.

The worst enemy of the Thule BMEWS people is the artic storms called "phases." These storms are caused by high winds which pick up the loose snow and carry it along. The higher the wind, the more snow there is in the air, and the poorer the visibility. In a phase III storm there seems to be more snow than air. This blowing snow is as fine as flour and will penetrate the smallest crack or crevice. During a severe storm, as much as a bushel of snow will blow into a building through a hole no larger than a pinhead.

A phase I storm has winds of not more than 35 miles per hour and visibility of not less than one-half mile. During these storms, the BMEWS people carry on their normal activity. A phase II storm has winds of 35 to 55 miles per hour and visibility of not less than one-quarter of a mile so that sky rangers carry on only the essential duties. Phase III is something else again. With winds up to 150 miles per hour, no one leaves the building or office. Emergency rations are broken out; desks and floors serve as beds until the storm is over. The really bad phase can last from five hours to three days.

At Thule, trackers will see the sun go down on the first of November. There will be twilights up until the 22nd of the month, then it will be dark until the 24th of January when they will again have twilight. On the 10th of February the sun will rise and they will have daylight and dark until the 24th of April when the sun will rise and not set again until the 22nd of August. It is a strange way to live . . . weeks of cold, blue-white sunless days and always the four gigantic fixed fan radars towering to the skies alongside mountainous cliffs of ice and snow. Close by is the "49" tracking radar, searching, scanning, all day, all night.

Thule trackers soon become accustomed to the fascinating wildlife whose wilderness they share. All year round there are foxes scampering about the mess hall looking for scraps of food. Arctic hare are equally unconcerned about the hu-

The BMEWS station at Clear, Alaska, is 70 miles southwest of Fairbanks. 700 Air Force and RCA personnel have a wide variety of off-duty recreational activities to break up the monotony of isolation.

man residents. In the summer, trackers searching for satellites and missiles will see snowfinch, plover, killdeer, ducks, geese, and even English sparrows. Millions of sea birds fill the skies—gulls, cormorants, skau, boobies, black duck, and many others. And below them in the ocean are seal, walrus, and whale. Pilots flying into the base see huge herds of the white whale—an animal that grows to thirty or thirty-five feet long.

CLEAR

The Thule BMEWS site, however, does not have a monopoly on furry visitors. At Clear, Alaska, which is seventy miles southwest of Fairbanks, as many as twenty-three rollicking black bears have been seen having their daily orgy at the garbage dump. Colonel Robert L. Harriger, commander of the 71st Surveillance Wing (BMEWS) also recalls the case of the nearsighted bear who plodded through the double plate-glass doors at the entrance to the main administration building. Having achieved his grand entrance, the bear proceeded to make himself comfortable at the door of the dining room, licking his wounds and ignoring the ensuing bedlam. However, he became quite amenable when the diners, assisted by a fire hose, asked him to leave.

It is a popular opinion at Clear that an animal capable of severing one's head from the body with the swipe of a paw is dangerous. However, one of the local "experts" states that this is not necessarily true of black bears, and says that a bear can be "spoofed" by shouting and clapping the hands. He proved his technique one evening upon encountering two of the animals as he left the dormitory. Quickly clapping his hands (from an upstairs window) our expert "spoofed" the bears into leaving, even though it took about five minutes and the smell of food from a nearby kitchen to do it.

Some of the hunters among the group have contemplated garnering a bearskin rug the easy way, but a former station commander, Colonel Edward H. Ellington, decreed that the only bear hunting on the main reservation would be done with a camera.

"The fools stand and let you walk up to them," says he. "It would be like shooting your pet dog."

Bear "spoofing" is only one of the sports enjoyed by the

Furry visitors at the garbage dump are a daily occurrence at Clear, Alaska. Bears are not shot, except with cameras. "The fools stand and let you walk up to them," says Colonel E. H. Ellington, station commander. "It would be like shooting your pet dog."

700 Air Force and RCA personnel at the Clear BMEWS site when they are not busy maintaining and operating their three "football field" fixed fan radars and newly constructed AN/FPS-92 tracker. There is the coveted membership in the "9th ADD Society of Stump Jumpers and Rafter Rollers" to strive for. This arctic version of the Limbo hits its peak at the Clear Sky Lodge a few miles from the BMEWS site. Trackers say anyone can join, but it takes a little physical effort as well as a bit of traveling—both horizontal and vertical—to make the team. The guide leads you to a long

log beam nestled in the rafters a goodly number of feet off the ground. The catch is that the log is quite thick and practically impossible to grip. You take the jump and make the grab. If you make it over the log—and you are granted innumerable tries—you'll join the group and receive an inscribed log from the island of Shemya (notable because Shemya has no trees). If you don't make it—well, back to the five B X exercise plan.

If all this seems odd, remember the lonely, desolate location of the Clear site. Think too of the 1600 consecutive hours of operation where they were completely "green" (no malfunctions that took them off the air). Families living in trailer camps are doing without many of the conveniences we take for granted. They grin and bear it. To help matters, they are always on the lookout for excuses to have parties.

There was the time when the sewers in the trailer camp were frozen for six weeks. When the thaw finally came, what better excuse could there be for a party? The sky rangers even elected a "Miss Sewer."

Along this line, there is also a big Alaskan sweepstakes classic which has been an annual event since about 1917. This is when everyone bets on the time and date that the ice in the river will break. The average pool runs about $106,000!

FYLINGDALES MOOR

Sky rangers at Clear become sourdoughs in every sense of the word while at Fylingdales Moor, England, the final link in the BMEWS system blanketing the top of the world, life takes on the traditional pattern of the old world.

Perched upon an 800-foot hill in the heather-covered Yorkshire moors near the North Sea coast, the three massive AN/FPS-49 bubble-shaped tracker units are operated jointly by the Royal Air Force Fighter Command and NORAD Commanders in Chief. By agreement between the two governments, RCA of America built the radars and they are now maintained by RCA of Great Britain.

THE NINTH AEROSPACE DEFENSE DIVISION'S 2ND SURVEILLANCE SQUADRON (SENSOR)

We have seen the widely contrasting sites of the BMEWS stations across the top of the world. But what of the sky rangers who operate the "2nd's" sensors in such areas as Moorestown, New Jersey; Shemya, Alaska; Oslo, Norway; Edwards AFB, California; Eglin AFB, Florida; and Cloudcroft, New Mexico? Perhaps we might sample an "extreme" at Shemya, Alaska.

THE BLACK PEARL OF THE ALEUTIANS

Imagine if you can a rocky island about two miles wide and four miles long, mountainless, windswept, fog-shrouded, far out in the Aleutian chain, 1,650 miles west-southwest of Anchorage, Alaska, and then ask yourself if you would like to spend a year there, tracking satellites. About a thousand men do, including Detachment 2 of our Second Surveillance Squadron of sky rangers.

Shemya, a part of the Semichi Island Group, was the scene of World War II activity against the Japanese. In May of 1943 Americans from the Fourth Infantry waded ashore under a thick cover of fog, after six hours of uncomfortable, sickening sailing from Attu. They dug foxholes and set up tents, only to discover they would have to excavate below the surface because of the high wind. The only sign of human life they found was a deserted Russian cabin and two graves of Russian Orthodox sailors. An airstrip was

BMEWS SITE III—An aerial view of the radar warning site at Fylingdales Moor, Yorkshire, showing the three radomes facing north and east to beam their signals over the North Sea. Part of the support area is in lower right, and a tropospheric scatter communications installation is in the center foreground. Radomes are as tall as 15-story buildings and house tracking antennae 84 feet in diameter.

whittled out of the tundra, and by September of that year, a crippled B-24 was able to land on it.

Today, the island is dotted with decaying buildings and installations of that era. It is too expensive to tear them down or move the equipment. "Whatever you do," say the trackers, "don't paint any of those buildings or they'll be considered usable again." A favorite stunt, they say, is to set fire to some of these old buildings as an offering to the gods so that the weather may be clear enough for the mail

Shemya, Black Pearl of the Aleutians. Sky rangers say there is a woman behind every tree and this is true—no trees! Mountainless, wind-swept, fog-shrouded, the tiny island is only two miles wide and four miles long. Trackers are supplied once a year by the "Mona Lisa" supply barge, and twice weekly by a MATS charter airplane.

plane to get in. There are about three times as many buildings falling apart as are in use.

There is a saying on Shemya that there is a woman behind every tree. This is true—because there are no trees. Twice a week MATS charter flights (Reeve Alaskan Airways) fly mail and supplies to the desolate island. On these flights are two stewardesses, the only women who ever come to Shemya. Needless to say, their arrival is a real occasion.

Sky rangers who are hosted by the 5073rd Air Base Squadron, Alaskan Air Command, are supplied with food and the necessities of life by the Mona Lisa barge which visits them once a year.

With the Bering Sea on the north and the Pacific Ocean on the south, the year round temperature range is from 20 to 50 degrees. Almost constant overcast conditions prevail, with winds as high as 100 knots. It is the only place in the world where heavy fog and high winds can set in simultaneously. In the winter, there is daily snow, sleet, or rain.

For the men on Shemya, there is no leave except for emergency reasons; no space-available trips to Japan, no stepping "outside" to Anchorage for a breather and a change of scene. It is a matter of sameness, day in, day out, for a full year. There is no place to go. You can walk from one end of the island to the other in an hour. Recreational facilities are very limited. What then is there to do to pass away the long lonely months?

Well, there are parties, and these are held in what Shemyans lovingly refer to as "smokehouses." Each unit on the island has its own smokehouse which serves as a kind of rough and ready lodge. The men are fiercely patriotic to their own individual smokehouse, since units stick pretty much to themselves. There is a certain amount of "hosting" between units, particularly when some fancy piece of scrounged equipment has been installed in the smokehouse.

The sky rangers are immensely smug about the flush toilet they "found" and installed.

Values change at Shemya. Things that money can buy don't mean much when you can't buy them no matter how thrifty you have been. Depression and personality problems are bound to crop up, especially when, for instance, a man due to rotate off the island is told he will have to wait a week longer. That week suddenly becomes an eternity.

The hobby shop is busy these days. For some reason, the men have taken a fancy to the art of making ceramic bunnies. Shemya has hundreds of ceramic bunnies in all sizes, shapes and colors.

Another curious pastime of the Shemya trackers is searching for Japanese glass fishing balls. Men spend hours walking along the bleak, black rocky shoreline, hoping and praying they will find one to add to the collection. Captain Robert Damon of the 2nd Surveillance Squadron is the number one salvager and current hero of the island, for in just two months he has collected a total of 24 of the glass balls.

The collecting has become almost a mania, a kind of luck symbol. Those who do not find their share are deeply bothered. They figure the cards are all stacked against them until a certain gray morning as they peer through the fog they see a green glass ball nestled invitingly in the partially hidden cove. Then everything is rosy again.

As we have mentioned about the military sky rangers and their civilian co-workers, a sense of humor and an appreciation of the ridiculous often save the day in an otherwise grim situation. Such is the case of Shemya's disaster-control plan. Directly in front of the Composite Building, the center of all island activity, is a six-foot round concrete slab. Attached to the slab is a long heavy chain. In the event of a national emergency where a disaster control plan must be put into action, personnel can pull the "Plug of Shemya" and sink the island!

The United States has come a long way in the business of tracking satellites. Only a few short years ago we depended on the relatively simple Minitrack system of radio inter-ferometers located on a straight line from Blossom Point, Maryland, to Santiago, Chile. We looked to the Baker-Nunn sky cameras to photograph the satellite against a star back-ground and we were greatly indebted to the volunteer Moon-watchers who peered through their inexpensive telescopes at dusk and dawn so that vital information could be re-ported to the proper centers. Gigantic radars that move mechanically have become commonplace. Now we have two new systems designed to feed volumes of information into SPADATS; systems that seem almost to be from a future century.

The new giant electronic eye, built by Bendix Corpo-ration's Radio Division, at Eglin AFB, Florida, is 324 feet long and as tall as a fifteen-story building. This huge installation is called ESAR (Electronically Steerable Array Radar). This *phased-array* radar system differs from the mechanically steered ones in that it remains stationary while its beams flick from horizon to horizon in fractions of a second. The "old" systems had to hold still and wait for their echo to bounce back from the object but the phased array with its many beams can use a few of its beams for target tracking, while the remainder search for new targets. It is, in every sense, a mass production system. Multiple receivers and transmitters make it possible to track many satellites up to altitudes of several thousand miles in one "glance." It can simultaneously detect, track, identify, and catalog orbiting satellites.

Authorities say the new AN/FPS-85 happens to be aimed towards the south.

ESAR (Electronically Steerable Array Radar) is as tall as a fifteen-story building. Built by Bendix Corporation, at Eglin AFB, Florida, this phased-array radar remains stationary while its beams flick from horizon to horizon in fractions of a second. Multiple receivers and transmitters allow it to track many satellites in one "glance."

Another fantastic space surveillance facility is the new electro-optical research laboratory, located on a 9,000-foot peak near Cloudcroft, New Mexico. The laboratory's main feature is a 48-inch diameter Newtonian optical telescope on a 3-axis precision tracking mount (originally a modified Baker-Nunn mount). The optical element is an image orthicon tube, which is similar to that used in a TV camera. The camera can photograph objects thousands of miles out in space with only the small amount of light given off by the moon. Its ASA rating (a fast "normal" film for home-use cameras would be about 200) is about one million.

There is no film to be developed with this new camera, since the picture is electronically "read" and information stored. The background of stars is automatically canceled out so that only man-made objects are observed. Its electronic accessories include precision position encoders, data recording, data-processing equipment, digital computer accessories for ephemeris calculations, and so forth.

The 70,000-pound telescope is housed in a special dome where temperature and humidity are controlled in order to precondition the telescope to the outside environmental temperatures before tracking begins. The outward appearance of Cloudcroft is much like that of an astronomical observatory. Originally planned for installation in the vicinity of Wright-Patterson Air Force Base, the New Mexico site was finally selected because of the better atmospheric transparency from the higher and drier location. Industrial haze, proximity of lighted city and suburban areas and prevalence of aircraft contrails in the Dayton area were major factors in choosing the New Mexico location. The forests surrounding the new site also minimize optical path disturbances due to thermal air currents.

And so, as the new phased-array radar and the electro-optical laboratory join the Spacetrack family of space monitors we wonder if our sky rangers are satisfied with the equipment they now have at hand. Can we be protected against possible missile and satellite attack from a hostile nation?

Colonel Robert W. Waltz, former commander of the 9th Aerospace Defense Division, says, ". . . unmanned Soviet space vehicles make sufficient passes over the North American continent in every 24-hour period to provide them—if they possess the technical capability—with nearly continuous surveillance of our terrain and the deployment of our strategic forces.

"We have observed with great interest the progress of the Russian space program. The recent Vostok III and IV operation may very well have been a practice which will eventually lead to the successful join up or 'docking' of two or more orbiting space vehicles. In our opinion, this docking operation will constitute the key to the successful construction and deployment of space stations. These could be used to keep the entire world under constant surveillance—perhaps even to clear the skies of other nations' space vehicles.

"Control of the space around this planet by an unscrupulously ambitious world power would be disastrous. . . ."

Colonel Waltz points out that SPADATS/Spacetrack can detect and identify, but ". . . we cannot fully determine hostile intent, nor can we destroy a hostile weapon in space."

As for the standoff bomber threat, Major General Arthur C. Agan states, "It is no secret that both our radars and our interceptors can go just so far and no farther. If an enemy can stand outside of our ability to detect or intercept and lob missiles against us, we've got a problem of serious dimensions.

"To combat this threat, responding to CINCNORAD's requirements in this area, ADC has been attempting to secure:

"More powerful radars, not only those that can see over the horizon by bouncing their beams off the ionosphere, but also more radars of the Frequency Diversity type. These send and receive impulses over alternating frequencies and thus have the ability to 'see through' electronic jamming.

"And most of all, an ability to get to a hostile carrier and destroy it before it can launch a weapon against us. . . ."

And, from Colonel Waltz again: "In the area of improved sensor capabilities—the logical progression is from earth-based to space-based facilities. The positioning of fixed position sensor devices—radar, optical, or heat-sensitive types—

will allow constant and instantaneous detection of ground-launched ballistic and space vehicles. . . ."

Although the Department of Defense has long since forbidden the release of information on SAMOS, according to *Parade* magazine, we have a number of surveillance satellites orbiting over the Soviet Union. These satellites, called SAMOS (Satellite and Missile Observation System)—contain equipment which photographs and records Soviet military installations. The film and tape capsules are routinely parachuted into the air somewhere between California and Hawaii. They are intercepted in midair by military aircraft or picked up at sea by the U.S. Navy. The Russians, as Colonel Waltz pointed out, are using similar satellites to photograph our installations.

And how are we to keep tabs on possible nuclear explosions in the atmosphere in defiance of the test-ban treaty?

The Air Force recently sent up the second of two Sentry satellites which maneuvered into station 65,000 miles above the earth to complete a space triple-play aimed at perfecting a foolproof means of detecting secret high-altitude nuclear explosions. The twin 292-pound Sentries are investigating techniques for establishing an operational network of six orbiting stations, which will electronically scan more than 200 million miles into space to chart natural radiation, so that a sudden burst of energy from a clandestine explosion could be readily spotted. The Sentries carry sensors to measure X rays, gamma rays, and neutrons, the products of a nuclear blast.

JOHNSTON ISLAND

A fact sheet put out by an unidentified alumnus of Johnston Island describes the area where the Air Force is now developing a nonnuclear anti-satellite system. With typical tongue-in-check it says:

Johnston Island is a small land mass on an atoll located some 3,600 miles south of St. Lawrence Island, Alaska and is about one-third of the way between Siberia and nowhere. . . . In 1942, the U.S. authorities declared Johnston to be filthy, putrid, hot, and unfit for human habitation; in short, a perfect place for a U.S. military base.

The island was annexed by both the Kingdom of Hawaii and the United States in 1958. However, in a sharp swap involving 200,000 grass skirts and five million gallons of fermented pineapple juice for 1,800 TV antennae, two southpaw pitchers, and a rare collection of Verdi arias by Elvis Presley, the U.S.A. took full custody.

There are no indigenous people now on the island. When the first Naval detachment arrived at Johnston, they were warmly greeted by the friendly natives, with such unspoiled sentiments as "You got gum, Joe?" and "You like my seester?" For some inexplicable reason, the natives amassed considerable wealth, and moved to Miami Beach, where they opened hotels.

The mean annual temperature is 98 degrees. The extreme temperatures recorded on the island are 97½ and 99. It has an average annual rainfall of 123 inches; nearly half of this falls in the period between April 24th and April 26th. Winds are nearly always. There are few trees, and hence a small canine population. Some lizards, hermit crabs, and other unfortunate entities not cleared for MATS flights to civilization, are found there. The large, nearly extinct, tropical gourmet shark abounds in the surrounding waters, together with the more Philistine species of moray eel.

Johnston boasts of two movie theaters, the Indoor theater showing those films rejected by television and the Outdoor theater showing those films rejected by the Indoor theater. . . . On the NCO Club's agenda for formal activities this summer are a maypole dance and interorganization jacks and tiddly-winks leagues. . . .

Johnston Island is obviously not the tropical paradise that sky rangers would choose for a tour of duty. Yet, according to *Missiles and Rockets* magazine, which enjoys a reputation for accuracy and serious reporting, as of February 1964, 1,930 people work on JI in total isolation. Of these, the Air Force totaled 275 military personnel and 825 civilians. The Department of Defense does not endorse this story, since both the United States and the Soviet Union have agreed to the United Nations resolution against atomic bombs in orbit.

The United States feels that it must have an answer to an orbital threat, should one be made, and that a nonnuclear capability would be consistent with the test-ban treaty.

According to the non-DOD reports, there are at least two types of programs under consideration. The first, a space-borne system, apparently has less accuracy potential than does the second system, which is ground-based. In the latter, a spacecraft would be launched for direct interception of a hostile vehicle. Ground commands would correct the trajectory, while final homing would be done by radar. Non-nuclear methods of destroying the enemy satellite could be by use of conventional explosives. Another method might be to spray pellets in a trajectory counter to that of the target. Or, it could be sprayed with a kind of paint that would damage the target's solar cells and thus degrade its power supply.

And where do our sky rangers fit into this "War of the Worlds," science-fiction drama?

One of these days, there will be a practice run to see if our satellite "insurance plan" works. We will actually destroy one of our own satellites. James Trainer, in *Missiles and Rockets* explains what will happen. *"Thors* and *Thrust-Augmented Thors* will be used to boost the maneuvering final stage—a modified *Agena D*—to satellite altitudes. . . . Special target vehicles launched from the Eastern Test Range (Cape Kennedy) at varying inclinations would give SPADATS the maximum opportunity to detect, track, and identify the target, and predict orbital parameters before the anti-satellite missile was sent aloft. . . ."

Obviously, without the extremely fine skills and equipment of our sky rangers, protection from hostile satellites could never be possible. With their present capability of detecting and predicting orbital elements of noncooperative (non-transmitting) satellites to within 50-100 feet after the first several passes, a ground-launched anti-satellite missile *could* hit the target. And even now, a precision three-site radar is being planned that will determine satellite orbits to within a *few feet* by triangulation.

Johnston Island. Even as it is being enlarged by 270 acres, with two nearby islands of 25 acres being created to house the wonders of the space age, the lampooning fact sheet beckons us to the misty past.

Until late in 1958, Johnston Island was a refuge for retired burlesque queens and ex-WPA employees. The Government then intervened, and it was used for advanced Flying Saucer research under the auspices of the staff of the Happydale Rest Home for the Mentally Bewildered. . . .

11

The Navy Space Surveillance
System (SPASUR)

IT was an odd scene that day at the Pima Indian Reservation. Even though the modern, bustling city of Phoenix, Arizona, was only a few short miles away, here, in the long adobe lodge, the tribal council was meeting in the age-old tradition of their forefathers. The men, most of whom were wearing levis, handsome handmade belts, and odd bits of native jewelry, were deeply tanned by the hot Arizona sun. Many of the faces were lined with the knowledge and wisdom of advanced age. There was a studied air of noncommittment, a kind of permeating mood of caution and suspicion, based on tribal tales and documented history.

The white man wanted to build something on some land that belonged to the Maricopa Pima tribe. This was not right, because by treaty no white man could lease, buy, or even use that land. It was a very important matter; one that called for serious deliberation. True, the lean blond naval officer had arranged with the paymaster for the Indians to be paid $250 per diem during the session, but that in itself did not obligate them to decide the matter in the white man's favor.

Captain Winfred Berg, USN, delegation of one for the cause of the new Space Surveillance System, stood near the wall and waited. Occasionally he glanced at the only other white man in the lodge, the manager of Indian affairs, who had brought him to this place. The return look said, "Keep your silence. The next move is theirs."

As he waited, Captain Berg thought of the events that led to this Monday afternoon meeting. It all began during the IGY when he had gone around to set up the original Minitrack stations which were designed to track Project Vanguard. That system of radio interferometers required that the satellite transmit a signal to the ground stations below.

This was all well and good until the Soviets launched Sputnik I. "And from now on, we'll launch one satellite a month," they boasted.

The Soviets did launch a second satellite in December, but there was no sign of the promised launches in January or February. Could they have launched them without our knowing? The White House wondered, and so did everyone else. It was obvious at this time that the existing Minitrack system would be of little military value. Something would have to be devised—and in a hurry—that would detect and track the silent space visitors.

It was on the 21st of May, 1958, that the Navy presented the idea of taking the Minitrack principal and making it active, that is, making it capable of transmitting a signal from the ground to reflect off a silent satellite. This would be done by setting up high power transistors on the ground. The system would be called SPASUR (although Roger Easton, "father" of SPASUR, prefers to call it Weapons System 434); it would function *all the time* and never be

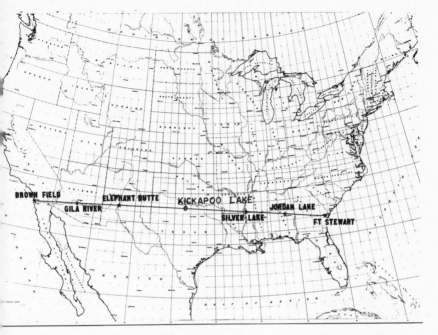

The Naval Space Surveillance System fence extends along a great circle line from San Diego, California, to Ft. Stewart, Georgia. Transmitter sites are located at Gila River, Arizona, Kickapoo Lake, Texas, and Jordan Lake, Alabama. The receiver stations are located at Brown Field, California, Elephant Butte, New Mexico, Silver Lake, Mississippi, and Ft. Stewart, Georgia.

turned off. Stations would run in a straight line from Fort Stewart, Georgia, to San Diego, California. It would be like a great picket fence across the southern part of our country, and anything that passed it was bound to be detected.

The idea was approved on the 21st of May, 1958, and the Naval Research Lab got the money with which to go to work, on the 19th of June. Berg will never forget those frantic days and nights when they worked round the clock, in the mud and rain and blistering sun in order to devise their SPASUR system. He chuckles over the logistics problems and how they were solved. Expediency was the keynote, as the Navy SPASUR men "stole" a radio transformer from Fort Monmouth, got hold of a conventional FM radio, converted it, and made the installation. Everyone was determined to have it operational by the end of July.

On the 31st of July, they were all set to turn it on when suddenly, sickeningly, it blew a transformer. It just wouldn't work. But the SPASUR men dug in, and hours later, on the "32nd" of July, six weeks from the time they'd gotten their money to build the system, it was turned on, and later, it became the first major contributor to SPADATS. No one ever accomplished such a feat before—or since.

But this was only a two-station facility, with a transmitter located at Jordan Lake, Alabama, and a modified Minitrack station at Fort Stewart, 250 miles to the east. If the picket fence were to be effective, it would have to reach all the way to the west coast. More sites would have to be chosen; transmitting stations which would emit beams of radio energy at 108 megacycles, and others which would be receiving stations.

With this in mind, Captain Berg drew a line across the map of the United States from Fort Stewart, Georgia, to San Diego, California, and then set out to select his sites. The problem was to get the sites selected very quickly. The satellite program was under way—SPASUR had to be operational as soon as possible.

Starting on the east coast, Fort Stewart, Georgia, was no problem as a receiver station. Nor was Jordan Lake, Alabama, as a transmitter site. Silver Lake, Mississippi, was swampy, and the local citizenry were skeptical at first; but with care and diplomacy a good piece of land was leased from the school district and the transmitter station could be erected. The transmitter site at Kickapoo Lake, Texas, fell nicely into line, rattlesnakes and all. Elephant Butte Reservoir, near Truth or Consequences, New Mexico, was next in line. And then there was Gila River, Arizona.

To Captain Berg's dismay, the Department of Interior called to say, "Sorry you can't have that spot in Arizona."

"But I must have it."

This was the first time Berg realized that he'd stumbled onto what appeared to be an insurmountable problem—an unbreakable treaty with the Pima Indians.

"But isn't there some way to get around the problem?" he asked.

"Sure," Interior told him. "One is to try to get an act passed by Congress." There was a pause, then, "You realize this is the last week of the current session. I don't think you'd make it."

"Well," suggested Berg, "Think of something else."

"All right. Join the tribe. Then it would all be legal."

Join the tribe! Just like that!

Now, as he eyed the young Council Chief, Morego, seated at the end of the table, he wondered how long the session would go on before he was called up. Twenty minutes elapsed, and still no one was paying any attention to him. The heat inside the lodge was fierce, but the suspense was the worst.

At last, Chief Morego stood up. A hush fell over the Council. What would he say? What would be the next step in this strange ritual? Hopefully, the Chief would pave the way by explaining the nature of the Naval officer's business.

No such luck.

Instead, the sole introduction consisted of "Captain Berg is here and has something to say to you." Period.

All eyes were now fastened onto the uniformed man as he began to explain what a space surveillance system was . . . why the country specifically needed to lease a bit of the reservation. "Well, you see, there are artificial satellites orbiting the earth and we need to set up antennas in order to pick up the signals . . ." His voice trailed off as he realized he was getting no response at all. It was as if he were talking to a blank wall.

But he had to go on in spite of the bland reception. Fifteen minutes later he decided to stop talking and try the question-and-answer approach.

Yes, the Indians did have some questions. What about the number of people that would be working at the station? Would there be any jobs available to the Pima Indian people? Finally, a very old man stood up. It was obvious that he was the senior member of the Council. The background chitchat quieted. Now there was total silence.

"Captain Berg," the old man said. "One question. Is anybody from the Army involved?"

This was it, Berg thought. The test, the loaded question. How should he answer? The question demanded a "yes" or "no" response. . . .

Berg pondered. Then with great care and caution he said, "It will be under the direction of the Military. A young Naval officer, probably a lieutenant, junior grade, or lieutenant, will be in charge."

Now Berg held his breath as the Council huddled together. The wait seemed an eternity but he was determined to mask his anxiety with an air of military dignity.

Then the answer came. It was unanimous approval!

Captain Winfred Berg was adopted by the tribe as their official Washington representative, a position he holds today. The Navy Space Surveillance system could use land on the Pima Reservation. It was great news, and now it was hard to believe that for a while matters had been so touch-and-go.

The Council adjourned, but as the men were filing out of the lodge, three old Indians came up and introduced them-

U.S. Navy Captain Winfred Berg joined the Pima Indian tribe in order to secure permission to build a SPASUR satellite-tracking station on the reservation. Today, Captain Berg is the tribe's Washington representative.

selves. They beamed with pride as they explained that they were all retired Navy firemen; two of them had served aboard the *Arkansas*, and one had sailed on the *Texas*. No wonder the voting had gone as it had.

On the drive back to Phoenix, the elated Berg still puzzled over the question he was asked. "That was a loaded one, wasn't it?" he inquired of the head of Indian affairs.

"Sure it was. The same thing happened to the Army a few years ago. They'd wanted to build an airfield, a part of which would infringe on Indian territory. They went through the same procedure, tribal Council and all. And the same old man stood up and asked his question. The question was, 'How many pounds in a sack of cotton?'

"The Army representative could not answer, the Council voted the project down, and from that time on, they've wanted nothing to do with the Army. The case has been in and out of the courts for years but the Indians have the law and a firm treaty on their side."

The SPASUR radar "fence" across the country continues to operate on about 98.5 percent efficiency with less than 1½ percent non-working time which is absorbed in the overlap of the units. It requires no look angles and does not depend upon any acquisition aid. No warning of an ap-

No warning of an approaching satellite is needed in order for SPASUR to detect, track and compute the orbit of any object passing over the United States. Reflections are picked up by antennae at the receiving stations, where the returning signals are translated into information which is then transmitted to a central computing center at Dahlgren, Virginia. From here, the information pours into SPADATS, at Colorado Springs. Shown here is the scoreboard.

NAVSPASUR (Navy Space Surveillance System) field station at San Diego, California. The system is designed for tracking noncooperating or "silent" satellites which may prove to be a threat to our National security.

proaching satellite is needed in order for SPASUR to detect, track, and compute the orbit of any object passing over the United States. Reflections are picked up by antennae at the receiving stations, where the returning signals are translated into information which is transmitted to a central computing center at Dahlgren, Virginia. From there, the information pours into SPADATS at Colorado Springs.

Under contract with the Naval Research Laboratory, Bendix Radio manufactured the radio receiving equipment for SPASUR and was responsible for building layouts and installation. Subsequently, Bendix Field Engineering was selected by the Navy to operate, supply, and maintain all seven stations in the system.

Roger Easton at NRL says, "We hope for four more stations in the near future. A receiving station at Red River, Arkansas, and one at Hawkinsville, Georgia. Also we're hoping to put up two research and development ones in south Texas: a transmitter at El Fronton, and a receiver at Raymondville."

Sky rangers in navy blue, or white, or khaki, with their gold braid gleaming in the sun, far from the waves and foam of the seven seas have wistfully added their nautical touch to the NAVSPASUR stations. Even though the sites are miles inland, surrounded by cactus, sagebrush and sand, the USN has found some bit of water, an obscure creek or puddle of some sort to name them for. Jordan Lake, Silver Lake, Elephant Butte Reservoir, Kickapoo Lake, and—the biggest stretch of the imagination—Gila River.

The U.S. Naval Space Surveillance System, the Navy's first operational *space* command, now owns its own 7090 Data Processing Systems—a big step from the digital mode of data processing. These, along with the newly developed Automatic Digital Data Assembly System (ADDAS) bring the ultimate goal of an automatic data transmission assembly and processing system close to fulfillment. SPASUR has come a long way from the jerry-built modification of Minitrack which in itself was a modification of AZUSA.

According to Captain Berg, we are just beginning to tap the many areas of application where SPASUR information can be used.

12

Sky Rangers at NASA

OCTOBER 19, 1899. Autumn leaves had turned to brilliant reds and gold. The New England air was crisp and invigorating as the lad of seventeen began his climb to the top of the cherry tree to clip the dead limbs.

It was a long hard climb up over the branches for a boy who was not as physically strong as others in his high school class. Childhood illnesses had prevented him from being active in sports and so he had turned to other pursuits: reading, writing, and developing a lively imagination. He became an expert on science fiction, particularly H. G. Wells' *War of the Worlds.* He read Jules Verne's books and had even gone so far as to rewrite a portion of Verne's *From the Earth to the Moon* to include a rocket launch instead of a cannon. And like the Wright brothers, he studied the flights of birds, wondering how the principal of aerodynamics could be applied to man.

This particular day (he later wrote in his autobiography) was "one of those quiet, colorful afternoons of sheer beauty which we have in October in New England. . . . As I looked toward the fields to the east, I imagined how wonderful it would be to make some device which had even the *possibility* of ascending to Mars, and how it would look on a small scale if sent up from the meadow at my feet. . . . I was a different boy when I descended the ladder. Life now had a purpose for me. . . ."

The boy's name was Robert Hutchings Goddard—destined to become the father of American rocketry. The boy did indeed construct models while concentrating on physics and mathematics in high school. He later attended Worcester Polytechnic Institute, where he graduated with top honors in physics and mathematics. He stayed on as an instructor while doing graduate work at Clark University, where in 1911 he received his Ph.D in physics. In 1912 he went to Princeton as a research fellow and worked on electrical theory (the subject of his Ph.D dissertation) during the day and on rocket propulsion theory during the evenings.

And so it was, all during his life: the singleness of purpose, the devotion to his dream of conquering the upper atmosphere, and ultimately, the void of space, through the use of rocket propulsion. It was Goddard who proved by static laboratory tests that a rocket could operate in a vacuum, and could therefore function in space. The Smithsonian published his extremely important paper, "A Method of Reaching Extreme Altitudes," in which he suggested that a rocket such as he was developing might someday be used to hit the moon. Milestone after milestone was reached during the 1920's, as he experimented with fuels, propulsion systems, and rocket design. During the 1930's, Dr. Goddard, with a small group of faithful followers, moved their rocket shop to Roswell, New Mexico, where they would have suitable firing grounds. There, he devised and patented a gyroscopic control for rockets and an ingenious system for cooling the combustion chamber (the fuel of the rocket acts as a cooling agent).

With the approach of World War II, the American military could see no potential in the use of rockets for offensive or defensive weapons. Later, the German V-2's proved this error in thinking and also revealed the great similarity to the liquid-fueled rockets pioneered by Dr. Goddard. The military did assign the American rocket genius the task of developing a jet assist takeoff fuel for aircraft (JATO) and for reviving his "bazooka" as an anti-tank weapon.

Alfred Rosenthal, Historian at Goddard Space Flight Center tells of the Goddard Legacy in *The Early Years.* "Robert Hutchings Goddard was as responsible for the dawning of the Space Age as were the Wrights for the beginning of the Air Age. Yet, his work attracted little serious attention during his lifetime. When the United States began to prepare for the conquest of space in the 1950's, American rocket scientists began to recognize the enormity of the debt which their science owed to the New England professor. They discovered that it was virtually impossible to construct a rocket or launch a satellite without acknowledging the work of Dr. Goddard. This great legacy was covered by more than 200 patents, many of which were issued after his death."

It was on the first of May, 1959, that NASA named its new Space Flight Center at Greenbelt, Maryland, in honor of Dr. Goddard. His name serves as an inspiration to all scientists and engineers who are engaged in the exploration of space. The motto of GSFC is appropriately taken from Goddard's high school oration:

It is difficult to say what is impossible, for the dream of yesterday is the hope of today and the reality of tomorrow.

NASA has launched some probes from Wallops Island in Virginia. Shown here is a close-up of the high-gain antenna at NASA's Wallops Station. This antenna is used to receive standard telemetry signals as well as television picture signals from the weather satellite, Tiros.

Today, only a few short years after Dr. Goddard's death in 1945, his dream of conquering space is becoming a reality. Instead of the New England meadow from which he would launch his boyhood invention, the United States now has three huge missile ranges: the Atlantic Missile Range (AMR), the Pacific Missile Range (PMR), each of which are on the coasts, and the White Sands Missile Range (WSMR) in New Mexico. In addition, NASA has launched some probes from Wallops Island in Virginia. Each range has distinct advantages. For instance, the AMR has 10,000 miles of shooting space over water where there is no danger of catastrophe to populated areas below. Also, AMR can take advantage of the earth's rotation so that launches have a slingshot effect. On the west coast, PMR can send vehicles into polar orbit because there is no land between it and Antarctica. Landlocked White Sands has the advantage of having test vehicles and components that are easily retrievable.

Tracking at these ranges is a highly complicated, precise business. At White Sands there are no less than nine AN/FPS-16 radars. Several types of optical equipment are used including the *facet-eye* camera. This camera consists of 25 long-barreled five-inch refracting telescopes linked to a similar number of TV-type image-orthicon tubes. It can photograph Venus and Jupiter in *daylight*. The images are then transmitted to indoor viewing screens and photographed with a plate camera.

White Sands also operates a station at Corpus Christi, for NASA's Manned Flight Network.

AMR and Cape Kennedy, are most familiar to television viewers because it is from here that all manned Mercury shots were launched. It is from the Cape that Gemini was launched and Apollo will depart this planet for the most spectacular explorations in the history of mankind. "Disneyland East," as comedian Mort Sahl described this popping-off point into outer space, is a 15,000-acre spit of sand and palmetto palms sandwiched between the Atlantic Ocean and the Banana River in southern Florida. The Atlantic Missile Range is operated under contract by Pan American World Airways, since it is Air Force policy to use private enterprise for nonmilitary operations. Pan American has subcontracted RCA for technical functions.

Practically the first thing you see at Cape Kennedy after rolling past the control gate is the ball-shaped domes of Azusa Mark II, which has been described as the Noel Coward of radar systems. This one is so sophisticated that it can track a missile for 2,000 miles and is accurate to within 40 feet at a distance of 150 miles.

Next you see the antenna fields of the Cape's complex communications systems and a LOX plant where liquid oxygen is manufactured. The weather is hot and humid in summer. Pelicans fly formation overhead, sandpipers strut uncertainly towards the water's edge, and in the bay are local fleets of shrimp fishermen. It is hard to reconcile primitive nature with the launch sites of Jupiter, Thor, and Minutemen, even though these space-age antiques have been around for a number of years. Driving down ICBM road you see the heart of the "big ones," Centaur, Atlas, and Titan; and beyond is Pad 14 where Glenn, Scott Carpenter, Wally Shirra, and Gordon Cooper climbed into their tiny Mercury capsules for their journeys into space.

From another pad nearby, Ranger took off for the moon and Mariner dashed for Venus. But the exciting, almost unbelievable sights are the Titan launch pads for the two-man Gemini flights, and beyond them, the 375-foot high Saturn gantries, higher than a 30-story building. This will be the sendoff point for the three Apollo moon voyagers.

The Cape is only one part of the picture. Downrange for

A camel lends an exotic touch to the Project Mercury tracking station on Grand Canary Island, off the northwest coast of Africa, where one of the eighteen world-wide tracking stations is located.

10,000 miles are the tracking stations where sky rangers track everything that is blasted off in their direction. Station staffs average about 140 men, including technicians and maintenance people. By making special arrangements with Great Britain, the Dominican Republic, and Brazil, tracking stations were built at Grand Bahama Island, Eleuthera Island, San Salvador, Mayaguana, Grand Turk, Puerto Rico, Antigua, St. Lucia, Trinidad, Fernando de Noronha, and Ascension Island. In addition, tracking ships which are converted troop carriers now called Advanced Range Instrument Ships (ARIS) fill in the gaps in the vast ocean.

Many of these sites are extremely isolated, so often it is necessary to ship in all food, living supplies and equipment to the islands. What would it be like to be a sky ranger at one of those faraway islands?

The Canary Islands, for instance, are located off the northwest coast of Africa, in the Atlantic Ocean, near the equator. This is a long way from Times Square, yet because of its vital equatorial location, the station must be manned by sky ranger experts.

Are the islands really named for the birds? Not at all, according to Chuck Rouiller, Goddard site director for the Grand Canary Island Manned Spacecraft Tracking Network station. The name is derived from the Spanish term meaning dog, since canines have always been plentiful here.

In addition to Rouiller, 23 Bendix contract personnel work at the station as well as 16 indigenous personnel. Sixteen of the Bendix personnel are married and live at Las Palmas, 40 miles distant from the station. Transportation back and forth is via NASA owned microbuses. As a kind of South American "repeat," six exbachelor sky rangers have married Spanish señoritas.

The station is equipped with the acquisition aid system

Syncom, a synchronous communications satellite, built by Hughes Aircraft Company, under direction of the Goddard Space Flight Center, has its orbital speed matched to the earth's rotation. Recently, it teamed up with the 20-year-old tug, Geronimo, for the first transmission of oceanographic data via satellite.

for initially acquiring the spacecraft, a radar system for determining the position of the spacecraft as a function of time, a telemetry system for monitoring the condition of the craft and the astronaut, a spacecraft communications system for correct communications with the astronaut, and another communications system which links the remote station with Goddard and the rest of the world.

Although widely spread, the three major launch sites of the United States cooperate and support one another, just as all of our sky rangers around the world pool their efforts and capabilities. Personalities and organizations team up, often for a single experiment. Such a strange bedfellow to the NASA space family has been a tired old Department of

Interior tugboat, the Geronimo. The 20-year old tug, converted for oceanographic research, teamed up with Goddard's Syncom II communications satellite for the first transmission of oceanographic data via satellite.

The data transmitted by Syncom concerned temperatures and salinity of water down to 3,000 feet in the Gulf of Guinea. Scientists aboard the Geronimo coded the data and transmitted it to NASA's station at Lagos, Nigeria.

NASA beamed the data to Syncom, and the satellite relayed the coded information to Lakehurst, New Jersey. Then the data went by ground lines to the National Oceanographic Data Center, Washington.

NODC computers compared the data with previously known information about the Gulf of Guinea. The computers confirmed that one of the Geronimo's instruments was malfunctioning—a condition already known to scientists aboard the vessel.

This and other information was routed back to the Geronimo by both satellite and conventional means. From Geronimo—to Syncom—to Washington—to Geronimo elapsed time was less than 45 minutes.

Geronimo has also helped Tiros weather satellites to measure worldwide surface temperatures of the oceans.

Another interesting tie-up between space explorers has been the Smithsonian Astrophysical Observatory's "Prairie Network" of 16 unmanned automatic-camera stations and NASA scientists. The SAO engineers working under a grant from NASA are literally going to catch a falling star—bright meteors—on film. When high-speed particles of varied sizes enter the Earth's atmosphere, trails of hot glowing gases are produced. Large particles cause bright meteors, or fireballs, and may have enough mass for a portion of them to reach the earth, intact. The surviving mass is called a meteorite. Of interest to NASA scientists are photographic measurements that will help determine how much mass a body loses when it enters the atmosphere at velocities comparable to those of reentering spacecraft. Photographs taken by the cameras will also give clues as to the origin of meteors. By calculating and extending the light trails backward into space, the scientist will be able to determine the particle's solar orbit, or whether it possibly came from the moon.

We wonder what early space pioneers such as Dr. God-

WORLDWIDE COMMUNICATIONS. Drawing illustrates how three stationary-type satellites can provide a global communications network with uninterrupted, 24-hour-a-day television and telephone service. Spacecraft are being developed by Hughes Aircraft Company for the National Aeronautics and Space Administration. Each satellite, at 22,300-miles altitude, can "see" a third of the globe. Microwave signals can be relayed via the satellites from any ground station to any other within the network. The satellites travel at a speed that is synchronized with the earth's rotation, and appear to hang motionless in the sky.

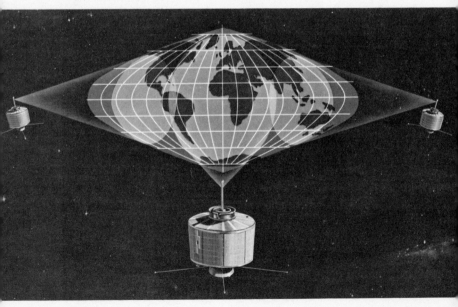

dard would think of today's efforts at conquering the far reaches of the sky. What would he think of sky rangers who had worked out the solution to tracking satellites that whing around the earth in cigar-shaped journeys, in polar orbits and in one-way trips to the moon and Mars? Each tricky flight must be precisely tracked, its scientific data returned, recorded and analyzed, if it is to be of any value.

NASA's SPACE TRACKING NETWORK FOR UNMANNED VEHICLES

For tracking unmanned vehicles in space, NASA depends primarily on three systems one of which is Minitrack radio-interferometer network of twelve stations which were built along the 75th Meridian during the IGY. This system is now a part of NASA's STADAN (Satellite Tracking and Data Acquisition Network) and it is used for tracking earth-orbiting satellites.

WIDEBAND DATA ACQUISITION NET

New members of STADAN are the Wideband Data Acquisition Net. Consisting of three huge 85-foot *parabolic antennae*, these "dishes" are designed to catch satellite signals that Minitrack is unable to "hear." Since spacecraft signals are rarely transmitted with a strength in excess of five watts (enough for a baby's night light) it is necessary that ground stations have large radio "ears." The principle is comparable to the cupping of the hand behind one's ear to hear a whisper.

Minitrack could not possibly gather all the *data* which will come from such sophisticated satellites as OAO (Orbiting Astronomical Observatory), OSO (Orbiting Solar Observatory), POGO (Polar Orbiting Geophysical Observa-

A new member of STADAN is the Wideband Data Acquisition Net, for tracking such sophisticated satellites as OAO, OSO, POGO, EGO, and Nimbus. The Rosman, North Carolina, Data Acquisition Facility has a huge 85-foot parabolic "dish" antenna.

tory), or EGO (Eccentric Geophysical Observatory). And certainly a Wideband Data Acquisition Net was required for Project Nimbus as it took television pictures of the earth cloud cover during its life span of twenty-five days. Since all Nimbus missions will have a polar orbit, the first station was built at Gilmore Creek, twelve miles north of Fairbanks, Alaska. This station provides coverage for seventy percent of the passes of a satellite in a polar orbit.

A second station in the new net is at Rosman, North Carolina. This station picks up an additional twenty percent of the passes of polar satellites. A third member of the Net is to be built at Canberra, Australia.

These giant "ears" can hear for *60,000 miles!* Even to those who are not addicted to space-age wonders, there is a kind of mystical aura surrounding them as ice and snow gather on their myriad struts and wires until they appear as mammoth Christmas tree ornaments. The sun sets, and the huge dish standing 120 feet high is silhouetted against the red-purple sky. And a romanticist could wonder if these sensitive marvels, tuned in to the highways of space, are telling us all the secrets they know.

Interestingly enough, the 300-ton "dishes" are moved by a hydraulic-drive system using a 75-horsepower and a 150-horsepower electric motor. Sky rangers simply move a duck-pin bowling ball which is set into the control panel to direct the antenna's position.

DEEP SPACE INSTRUMENTATION FACILITY (DSIF)

Imagine taking a long pointer and aiming it at a dot on a blackboard from a distance of twenty feet. How close could you come to that dot?

This in essence is what our sky rangers are doing—successfully—with their powerful radars of the Deep Space Instrumentation Facilities. The mission of this network is the tracking, data acquisition, and control of all NASA unmanned lunar and planetary spacecraft; that is, those in deep space. The Jet Propulsion Laboratory (JPL) operated by the California Institute of Technology has been given the responsibility by NASA for running the Network Control Center at JPL in Pasadena, California, along with the tracking stations at Goldstone, near Barstow, California, at Johannesburg, South Africa, and Woomera, Australia. The latter two are manned by indigenous personnel.

Quietly listening, probing deeply into space, the specialized equipment at the Goldstone, California, Facility is far away from automobile ignitions, which would clutter the delicate messages from space; no aircraft radios, power lines, or commercial radio transmitters disturb this DSIF tracking mission.

And why these particular locations?

Once a probe reaches a good distance in space, it is like the moon and the sun. It rises and sets because of the earth's rotation. Therefore, DSIF facilities must be located 120 degrees apart around the earth in order to have the probe in view at all times.

Quietly listening, probing deeply into space, the specialized equipment must also stand far from interfering background noise. Goldstone Facility is perfect in this respect, although as we have noted earlier, it is far from pleasant living for the men who run the stations. Here in the heat of the Mojave desert, as winds, sand, and isolation close in, there are no automobile ignitions cluttering the delicate messages from space; no aircraft radios, power lines, or commercial radio transmissions.

At Goldstone, there are actually three stations within a seven-mile radius. The main station is called Echo. It has an 85-foot diameter polar mount antenna, capable of tracking at angular rates of one degree per second. Polar mounts, like large radio telescopes, capture signals from a point straight in front of them. To track a space vehicle, sky rangers simply point the telescope in the direction of the strongest signal.

Subsystems include a sensitive phase-locked receiver with a low noise parametric amplifier, a 10-kw maximum power transmitter and associated data-handling and instrumentation systems.

Pioneer station at Goldstone has an identical big dish, but no transmitting capabilities. It is used mainly for research and development of advanced components and systems, or as supplementary tracking antennae for spacecraft. Venus station consists of an 85-foot diameter azimuth-elevation antenna with Cassegrain type feed. There is also a 35-foot dish for special testing of communications equipment. A 100-kw transmitter is being developed to communicate to the far reaches of the solar system.

The equipment for the Australia and Africa facilities is similar to Goldstone's, although there are some variations. These sites operated from trailers until their buildings were completed. All the equipment was broken down in pieces, shipped by air, then reassembled by steel workers from the United States, under the expert direction of JPL sky rangers.

Are the DSIF trackers satisfied with their present setup?

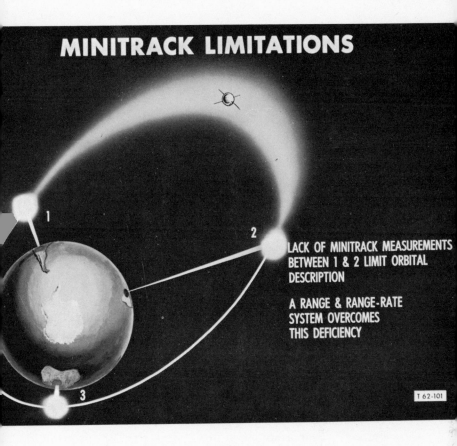

MINITRACK LIMITATIONS

LACK OF MINITRACK MEASUREMENTS
BETWEEN 1 & 2 LIMIT ORBITAL
DESCRIPTION

A RANGE & RANGE-RATE
SYSTEM OVERCOMES
THIS DEFICIENCY

T 62-101

As usual, there is restlessness and worry about tomorrow. What would happen if several deep probes were put up simultaneously? At the moment, these facilities can track two of them for 24 hours a day, but a third one would amount to 36 hours of surveillance. A day is just not long enough for that job. For this reason, JPL is arranging for other sites to be added to the DSIF net.

Tracking facilities, as we have seen in other systems, must

be constantly updated, improved, and rearranged, in order to keep ahead of planned space shots. Shirley Thomas explains this problem in her book *Satellite Tracking Facilities*: "If a vehicle is launched to Mars, and the travel time there will be many months, tracking and data acquisition facilities must be allocated full time during critical periods of flight, and at least on a periodic basis during the entire flight. Plans are now being made for exploration farther out, to the other planets. Tracking facilities, which require a long period to construct (a 210-foot dish requires five years), must be ready when the launch time for these probes approaches."

RANGE AND RANGE RATE

A new Goddard tracking system—range and range rate—and an old but indispensable human asset—the skill of the professional—are solving the riddle of how to track satellites which are in highly eccentric orbits. These "birds," winging around the earth in their elliptical journeys, can be tracked by Minitrack stations when they are near the earth, but by the time they have reached apogee of perhaps 50,000 miles, conventional tracking accuracies are not good enough. Accuracy is important because a vital part of all scientific satellite-positioning data is the satellite velocity, relative to its location in space, at which various experimentation measurements are made.

Engineers of Goddard's Systems Development Branch tackled the problem and came up with the idea that if the satellite were equipped with a transponder that would receive on one frequency and retransmit to the ground station on another, the time delay in the signals would indicate the satellite's distance (range). So far so good. But what about velocity? To solve this problem, the Doppler-shift principle (remember the *eeeooong* of the train whistle?) was adopted.

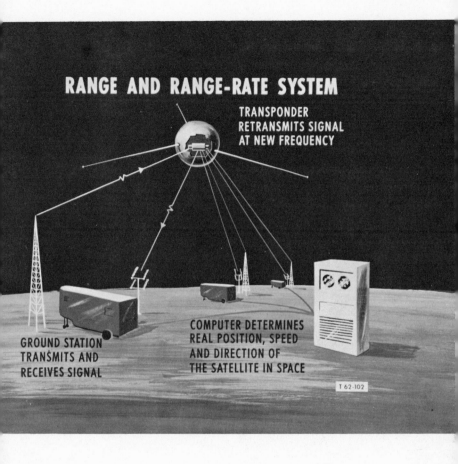

RANGE AND RANGE-RATE SYSTEM

TRANSPONDER RETRANSMITS SIGNAL AT NEW FREQUENCY

GROUND STATION TRANSMITS AND RECEIVES SIGNAL

COMPUTER DETERMINES REAL POSITION, SPEED AND DIRECTION OF THE SATELLITE IN SPACE

T 62-102

R&RR (range and range rate) requires the use of three mobile units to house the systems which are fabricated by the Motorola military electronics division. The beauty of the mobile units is that they can be easily moved to different geographical areas for future satellite programs.

R&RR proved its value and versatility in locating the missing communications satellite Syncom I. In that shot, the first touchy decision came for sky ranger Pete Engels when he discovered that Syncom's beacon signal was too faint to lock onto the autotrack receiver which would have provided sufficient power for the antennae to follow the spacecraft.

What to do? "We'll switch to the signal level output from the range-and range-rate receiver to get a visual indication of the spacecraft signal level."

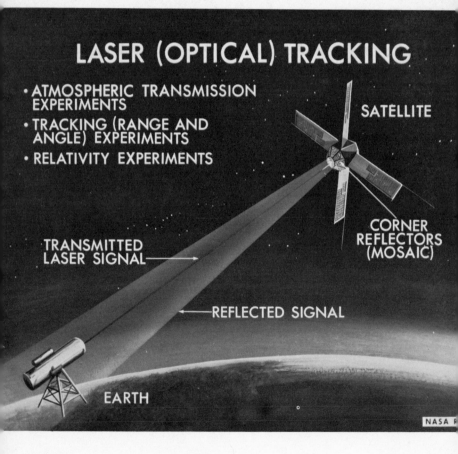

LASER (OPTICAL) TRACKING

- ATMOSPHERIC TRANSMISSION EXPERIMENTS
- TRACKING (RANGE AND ANGLE) EXPERIMENTS
- RELATIVITY EXPERIMENTS

SATELLITE

CORNER REFLECTORS (MOSAIC)

TRANSMITTED LASER SIGNAL

REFLECTED SIGNAL

EARTH

NASA

The second big decision Engels faced was when the signal level from the spacecraft became so low the signal failed to lock onto one of the seven range tones, the 20-kilocycle sidetone, which is essential to obtain ranging data. "Switch off the 100-kilocycle sidetone and channel its power to the 20-kilocycle tone," he told the trackers. It was a tense moment. Syncom had to be found and made to keep working for its earthly masters. But at 22,000 miles, this satellite is very faint, only as bright as a star of the 17th magnitude, or 25,000 times fainter than the smallest heavenly body visible with the naked eye. It's also pretty small: 28 inches across.

Could Engels and his sky rangers find this needle in the space "haystack"?

The drama of the search pattern for locating the spacecraft continued, as R&RR's data on the position and velocity of Syncom told engineers that the apogee kick motor would have to be fired 10 minutes before the time set in the timer clock in the satellite.

Using this information, and assuming that the velocity contributed by the kick motor to be either nominal, plus 100 feet per second, or minus 100 feet per second, three acts of search patterns were drawn up by Dr. Joseph Siry, head of Goddard's theory and analysis office.

Using the patterns, the Boyden observatory at Bloemfontein, South Africa, with its big Super Schmidt telescope, entered the search, along with other tracking stations and observatories within possible sight of the spacecraft. And sure enough, Sycom turned up almost exactly at one of the predicted points.

LASER

The term LASER stands for "Light Amplification through the Stimulated Emission of Radiation." In other words,

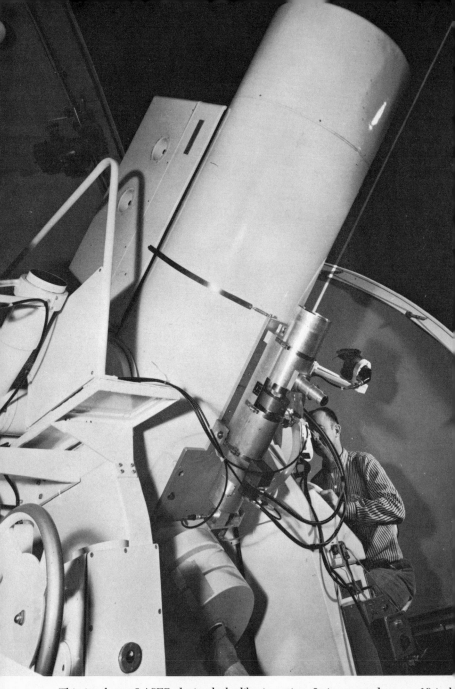

This is what a LASER device looks like in action. It is mounted on an 18-inch optical tracking telescope atop a 60-foot tower. The LASER emits a highly concentrated and "coherent" beam of light—about the size of a pencil—which will reflect off the glass prisms mounted on the satellite.

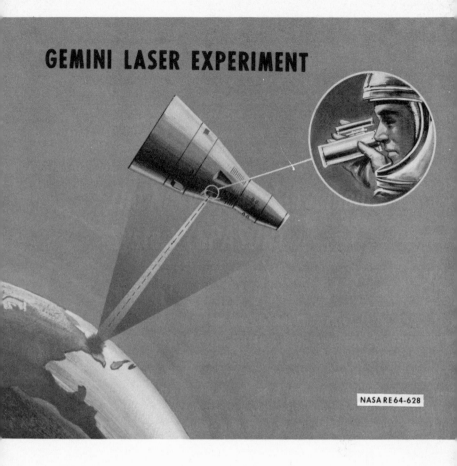

GEMINI LASER EXPERIMENT

NASA RE 64-628

LASER is very much like the science-fiction ray gun of Buck Rogers and other comic-strip characters. It emits a highly concentrated and "coherent" beam of light, about the size of a pencil, by energizing the chromium atoms in a six-inch long synthetic-ruby rod.

This particular device was designed and built by the Goddard Space Flight Center and will be used to track the Ionosphere Beacon Explorer Satellite. Mounted on the satellite will be an array of fused silica glass reflectors (360 one-inch-diameter glass prisms called "cube-corner" reflectors) designed to return back to earth light signals aimed at it from a LASER. An 18-inch optical tracking telescope atop a 60-foot tower at Wallops Island, Virginia, will find the satellite, and the LASER will then direct a pulsing beam of light toward the satellite at a rate of one "flash" per second. If the experiment is successful, results will lead to a more definite determination of the earth's shape and to the development of improved systems for future optical tracking and communications.

13

Manned Space Flight Network

IT was only a few short years ago that scientists were climbing mountains in pursuit of evasive knowledge about the earth, its upper atmosphere, its air ocean, and the space beyond. They loaded aircraft and balloons with instruments, and devised elaborate ground equipment, hoping to learn about particle and radiation bombardment of the earth and upper air. These techniques were helpful, but primitive in comparison with satellites. Rocket and satellite research has helped to pull aside the veil which since time began has obscured the true meaning of the stars.

There are many reasons why artificial satellites are orbiting the earth today, and why probes are sent into deep space. Communications, weather, reconnaissance, measuring and testing with myriad instruments, photographing the earth and neighboring planets . . . all so that someday, man himself could explore new worlds beyond earth. Someday, man will find out if there is life on Mars, what lies under the cloud cover of Venus and what the other side of the moon looks like.

But before man could undertake space travel he needed to know about conditions in space and certain physical facts he would encounter away from earth. Satellites were the mechanical messengers that sent back information that made manned space flight possible. The first step in gathering vital information lay in locating and tracking the satellites. The electronic ears of Minitrack stations strained for the tones of the satellites' tiny radio transmitters. The indented eye of precision tracking cameras pierced the night sky to record the flights of the speeding satellites. Professionals joined volunteers in the exciting job of predicting the satellites' orbits.

Dedicated sky rangers developed more sophisticated systems for reaching out into space to monitor their traveling herd of satellites. And then suddenly, or so it seemed, the time had arrived for a man to be strapped down in a contour seat aboard a tiny milk-can-shaped capsule and shot out into space. Project Mercury, crude as it was, became the culmination of man's ancient dream of space flight. Organized on October 7, 1958, its goals were:

1. To place a manned space capsule in orbit around the earth,

2. To investigate man's reactions to, and capabilities in, this environment,

3. To recover both the capsule and the pilot safely.

Never before had the sky rangers' responsibilities been so awesome. Tracking mechanical birds orbiting the earth had been a challenge to ingenuity and dedication. Minor mistakes could be made in orbital predictions, and if the satellite were out of sight and sound on a pass, it could be picked up the next time around.

Not so with a manned flight. When a human life is at stake, accurate information must be available in real time— as it happens. Sky rangers have to know the velocity of the

MANNED SPACE FLIGHT NETWORK (MSFN)

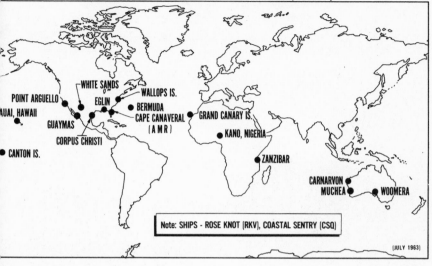

Note: SHIPS - ROSE KNOT (RKV), COASTAL SENTRY (CSQ)

(JULY 1963)

orbiting spacecraft, its position, accuracy, and the condition of the man himself, so that emergency corrections can be made. Because urgency is the keynote in every phase of the project, a thoroughly reliable back-up system is necessary. Then too, there must be voice communication from the time the man enters the capsule until the very end of his flight. And the manned flight was scheduled to span three continents and three oceans!

To remind workmen assigned to Project Mercury that a man's life depended on the reliability of the equipment, a tiny figure of the winged god Mercury was stamped on each component of the capsule.

How did sky rangers set about establishing such an elaborate worldwide tracking network for manned flights?

Into the wilderness, the jungles, and the deserts moved the sky rangers, in order to set up tracking stations for the Manned Space Flight Network. Chwaka, 17 miles from Zanzibar City has been discontinued for political reasons.

Once the orbital path of the spacecraft was determined, the experts took a long hard look at the existing facilities, and another look at the calendar. One year was their allotted time. It would be a tough job, and sky rangers knew they would need to use everything they had in operation—and more too. The military would be called upon to assist with their stations and equipment; foreign governments would be approached for permission to erect stations in key locations.

In order for the spacecraft to be in touch with ground stations for five minutes out of every fifteen, the following locations were decided upon:

Bermuda; Mid-Atlantic Ocean Ship; Canary Islands; Kano,

Nigeria; Zanzibar; Indian Ocean Ship; Muchea, Australia; Woomera, Australia; Canton Island; Hawaii; Point Arguello, California; Guaymas, Mexico; White Sands, New Mexico; Corpus Christi, Texas; and Eglin Air Force Base, Florida. Station Number One was the launch site, Cape Kennedy.

Reminiscent of the IGY when Minitrack stations and SAO optical tracking sites were being established, the industrial team under contract to NASA, along with State Department representatives, met with foreign officials to obtain permission for building the new stations. There were sensitive areas to be sure, with political tightrope-walking in countries where the wrong diplomatic approach could have yielded a strong "no." But this was a peaceful scientific effort, one which would provide stimulus to local scientists and jobs for native workers. Fortunately for our manned space project, all the sites were granted.

Into the wildernesses, the jungles, and deserts moved the sky rangers. Trees were hacked down as chattering monkeys swung by their tails nearby and scratched their heads in bewilderment. Camels stood aside docilely as roads were built through the brush and tall grass. Families living in grass huts as they had for centuries wondered at, but trusted in, what these strangers were doing.

In one country where the government wanted to spread the employment among as many people as possible, all mechanical earth-moving equipment was forbidden. Much to the frustration of sky rangers working on a tight time schedule, only woven baskets and wooden shovels could be used to dig foundations for the station buildings. As "guests" they dared not call on their trusty bulldozers to do the job.

At last the $60 million global network was completed and turned over to NASA. Western Electric Company headed the team. Other members were Bell Telephone Laboratories, Inc.; the Bendix Corporation; Burns and Roe, Inc.; and

A Nigerian tribesman playing a Nausa Flute. Many Nigerian nationals are employed at the Kano tracking station.

International Business Machines Corporation. At the same time, the Lincoln Laboratories of MIT advised and assisted on special technical problems related to the network. A fantastic job accomplished by Western Electric was the creation of the communications facility to connect all the stations and provide two-way transmission of information. This consists of 102,000 miles of teletype, 60,000 miles of telephone, and 15,000 miles of high speed data circuits. Additional facilities include equipment for acquiring the spacecraft; long-range radars for tracking; telemetry equip-

Two Nigerians watch twin- and quad-helix antenna at Kano swing to acquire the necessary capsule.

Boy on camel's back is etched against African skies with NASA space-tracking antenna as a modern backdrop. Photo typifies the globe-girdling tracking and communications system that links many nations in space effort.

ment for control from the ground, if necessary; and voice channels for ground-air-ground communications.

The focal point, or "think" center of this integrated tracking and data-acquisition system is Goddard Space Operations Control Center, which determines and predicts satellite orbits and serves as the hub of a voice network (NASCOM) which links all stations of the network. Triplexed, high-speed computers, each with a "real time" capability, make constant flight contingency recommendations, predict flight paths, determine the time to initiate reentry, and predict the impact point of the capsule on a near-instantaneous and continuous basis throughout the mission.

Six of the stations and two ships have command capability, that is, they can actually control the capsule from the ground, should the astronaut be unable to do so himself. This command was used during the MA-5 shot with the chimpanzee Enos. Telemetry from the capsule told the sky rangers at Point Arguello that too much fuel was being used, so they sent a command to fire the retro-rockets and bring the capsule down after two orbits instead of the planned three. Both the capsule and the astrochimp were recovered.

Equipment at all the stations in the Manned Space Flight Network is as uniform as possible, so that sky rangers can go from one place to another and continue their work in a routine manner. Carefully screened and highly trained, these men carry their responsibilities for astronauts' lives with sober concern. They know that as the capsule approaches Bermuda after launch, their word of "go" or "no go" determines whether or not it will be put into orbit. From then on, until the reentry and impact occurs, a man's fate is in their hands.

What exactly does occur in a Mercury flight as it blasts off the pad at Cape Kennedy?

Take the flight of astronaut Gordon Cooper, whose 44-hour, 22-orbit globe-girdling mission was so dependent upon the perfect functioning of the worldwide tracking and data-acquisition network.

From the instant that Cooper was shot into space, high-speed data lines carried his progress report from the Cape and Bermuda to the computers at the Goddard Space Flight Center. The "think" center then shot back the computers' answers to the Manned Space Flight Control Center.

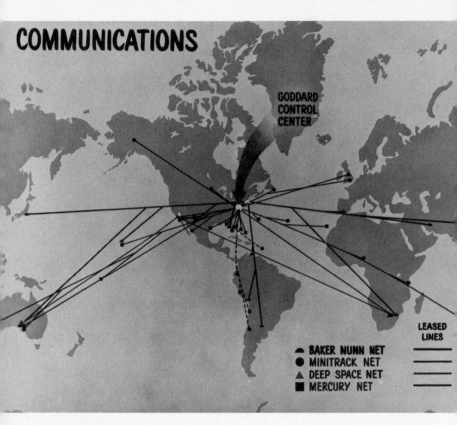

COMMUNICATIONS

GODDARD
CONTROL
CENTER

BAKER NUNN NET
MINITRACK NET
DEEP SPACE NET
MERCURY NET

LEASED
LINES

Radars at the Cape, talking in language which the computers could understand, continued to feed the busy machines. Likewise, the computers fed their answers to the plotting boards. The "language" is a digital data code which tells the electronically driven plotting boards how the graph should be plotted as to the spacecraft's trajectory. Cooper's constantly changing impact point, his booster functions . . . all were displayed for study.

Bermuda said "go"—into orbit. Now all the stations around the world were given acquisition data for radar alignment. Controllers at Mission Control Center were in voice contact. Cooper settled back for the flight of a lifetime.

Meanwhile, each site he flew over snapped to attention. Voice and telemetry communications from the orbiting vehicle told the sky rangers that all was well. This information was flashed over worldwide NASCOM circuits to Goddard, processed instantaneously, and fed to the Control Center. Orbit after orbit, hour after hour, trackers stayed with the heroic astronaut until at last he was brought down safely.

What finer tribute could be paid the faithful sky rangers than Gordon Cooper's sincere thanks. "It is certainly comforting to know, when you are out there, that the world's

View of Mercury Room at the Naval Missile Facility during a simulated flight test. One of the seven Mercury astronauts could be at the center position of the console during orbit. He directs voice communication with the orbiting astronaut and can reset the command switch for capsule reentry.

finest communications network and the finest electronic facilities that man can devise are functioning with a fantastic computer complex that will allow the onboard systems specialists to break out their diagrams and tell you immediately what your situation is in the event of trouble. . . . Without this marvelous organization, it might have been a little more than difficult to get back home."

GEMINI-APOLLO

The moon hangs as a frail new sliver. At the edge of the sea, the rocket steams ominously in the faint breeze before dawn, unable to stifle the boiling of the liquified hydrogen and oxygen being pumped aboard. Danger hangs in the air, palpable as a thunderstorm. Despite years of familiarity, liquid hydrogen remains a cold and sullen beast—barely containable at best, uncontainable at worst. Breaking loose from its tanks high in the upper sections of the Saturn, the hydrogen could drench the launch pad and acres around in fire. The vehicle creaks, crackles and whines as the frigid and bubbling fuels pour in, chilling it down. It grows from its empty weight of 250 tons to its flight weight of 3,000 tons.

Near the tip of the rocket 320 feet up, partially wreathed in mist from the fuel, three men file across a bridge that juts from the umbilical tower. The astronauts! Quickly they're gone into the Apollo cone's door. A cloud of technicians obscures the opening.

In a distant blockhouse, a few dozen men in partnership with a computer continue with their countdown. It's an easier task now than in the Atlas and Titan day, before the time of automatic checkout machinery. In those days of the grueling manual countdowns, fatigue and tensions constantly threatened to leave something unattended to. The scores of "go" replies that punctuated Mercury countdown are reduced here to only a few, as the automatic machinery samples the signals from hundreds of

The manned Flight Network Tracking Station, Bermuda has the responsibility of saying "go" or "no go" into orbit for a manned flight.

electrical wires leading into the Saturn's interior, taking pulse and temperature, seeing to it that the rocket's brain, nerves and muscles are functioning. Gradually Saturn grows more and more awake under the prodding of the handlers' fingers, the urgings of the computers. The nerves of the stirring giant send floods of signals coursing into the blockhouse as fuel systems are pressurized, electronics systems activated, valves open, others close, pumps begin whirring.

Atop this vast and audibly seething assembly, the three astronauts have climbed into their couches for the four-hour wait until launch time. Bands of webbing are fastened across their torsos and their upper arms and legs, to hold their bodies in place against forces from any direction. Reclining side by side in the standard knee-high position, they watch a few instruments flicker amid the dozens on the broad panel that extends across the width of the capsule before their faces. From time to time they speak quietly to the groundlings and to each other. They feel the small tremors in the craft, reminiscent of any vehicle that is being made ready for travel: complaints as its metal adjusts to thousands of tons of cold fuel, faint hums and vibrations as the main engine nozzles far below are swung back and forth in their mountings to test their steering action, clicks of electrical switches and relays. The pilot-commander lies preoccupied with the signals echoing in his helmet, with the red and green lights, and the few instruments that could indicate something wrong.

For Gemini and Apollo flights, sky rangers will have the responsibility of tracking two vehicles at the same time. In Gemini, display-command systems will be as much as 40 times more complex than those used in Project Mercury. Tracking Apollo will involve knowledge gained during Projects Mercury and Gemini.

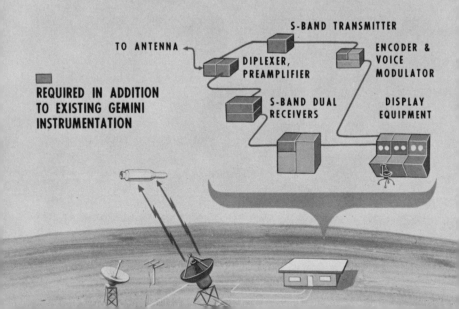

TYPICAL 30 FOOT ANTENNA GROUND STATION FOR APOLLO

S-BAND TRANSMITTER

TO ANTENNA

ENCODER & VOICE MODULATOR

DIPLEXER, PREAMPLIFIER

REQUIRED IN ADDITION TO EXISTING GEMINI INSTRUMENTATION

S-BAND DUAL RECEIVERS

DISPLAY EQUIPMENT

In his left hand, he holds the lever with which he can ignite the escape rocket and jerk them all four thousand feet up and away from whatever trouble the chemicals below have in mind. In the right-hand couch, the systems manager monitors his board for symptoms in Apollo's electrical, communications, life-support, control, propulsion, and navigation systems. The co-pilot in the middle watches his section of the board, partly a duplicate of the pilot's. Mostly he is concerned with the health of the inertial guidance system. This navigational device, with its acceleration-sensing pendulums, is mounted on a "stable platform," so equipped with gyroscopes as to remain oriented in space despite all the twists and turnings of a spacecraft, giving a reference in the wild universe that awaits these men a few minutes hence. The co-pilot sees to it that the device's computer brain tends to business, keeping its mind on the earth, the moon and the time of day.°

It is difficult to realize that this scene, so aptly portrayed by Tom Alexander in *Project Apollo* is scheduled to take place before 1970. At a cost of $20 billion, Apollo will put three American astronauts on the moon for a looksee at our closest space neighbor. Think of the responsibilities our sky rangers have, first with the preliminary flights of the two-man Gemini vehicle, and later the three-man Apollo! Now they must keep track of *two* vehicles at all times, as they rendezvous in space!

The perfect flight of GT-3, America's first 2-man space flight is now a proud chapter of history, thanks to the sky rangers who rode herd on the Molly Brown. These men whose responsibility it was to keep constant tabs on Gus Grissom and John Young as they orbited through space, had undergone a tremendously intensified nine-month training course at the Wallops Island tracking site. Only the real "pros" were accepted for this schooling and not all of them wound up as Knights of the Royal Order of Geminiers. Some

° Tom Alexander, *Project Apollo*. New York, Harper & Row, 1964. All rights reserved. Used by permission.

The Goddard Space Flight Center is studying the possible repair of spacecraft while in orbit. It is possible that in-orbit repair will one day prove to be more economical than second launches and the replacement of whole satellite systems. This is a concept of how the OAO may be repaired in orbit. Sky rangers on earth will be monitoring this.

just didn't quite make it, but those who did are proud to be terrenauts in the age of extended space travel. The reason for the Gemini trackers' added training lay in the complicated nature of the mission itself, and the difference between it and its predecessor, Project Mercury.

The Gemini display command system, for instance, is 40 times more complex than that used in Project Mercury. More than 500 lights, meters, switches, and dials are needed to monitor the Gemini vehicles, and later, the Agena spacecraft.

The equipment developed by Bendix Corporation's Bendix-Pacific division under a $5-million Goddard contract for the manned spaceflight-tracking network has been installed for both Gemini and Agena capsules. These Ben-Pac Consoles are at ten different sites around the world.

And then there were new and interesting trajectory computation problems facing sky rangers at Goddard's Data Operations Branch. No longer is there a beginning, middle, and end of flight, as with Mercury. Now, with the Molly Brown, computations had to be tailored to a new booster, the Titan II, which consists of two stages, the second stage of which is ignited in flight.

Another change was that launch abort modes had to be revised, because the escape tower was replaced with an ejection seat.

Aboard the spaceship, a propulsion system which allowed the crew to maneuver in space made it necessary for the terrenaut sky rangers to compute new propulsion parameters. In other words, if the Gemini capsule went too far out of its planned voyage, experts on Mother Earth could bring it back to a safe path.

Then too, there was the intriguing problem of reentry point. With Mercury, the astronaut simply fired his retrorockets at a specified time, and landed in a predetermined area. The Gemini crew using lift during reentry into earth's atmosphere had a certain amount of control in selecting their landing point. Instead of an impact point, the Gemini spacecraft had a landing "footprint" of 500 miles by 100 miles. To compute the spacecraft landing point, the computers had to know the lift the spacecraft was experiencing at all times during the reentry. Obviously, since Gemini can maneuver in flight, it is no longer a situation of a "captive audience" out there in space, and the task of selecting an optimum recovery area is one of the more difficult to be faced by sky rangers.

And what of Apollo?

The tracking system for the moon voyagers is still in the working stages. As in the past, all sky ranger experience will be called upon—all operational Manned Space Flight Systems will be needed to follow the first voyage of earthlings as they blast off to the moon. Every skill, every bit of equipment which has been developed and installed in remote corners of the world will be called into action. Our pioneer voyagers to the moon will owe their success—their very lives—to the dedicated work of the ground control stations on earth.

According to *Missiles and Rockets*, NASA and the Department of Defense plan to spend $160 to 170 million for the Apollo Unified S-Band Network which will support all orbital and lunar explorations.

The Unified S-Band will provide a single global system of precision tracking and two-way voice and data communications. The actual tracking will be via range and range rate. Three types of stations will be used; a 30-foot diameter dish with one complete S-band system for Apollo Command Module support; a duplexed 30-foot diameter dish with dual S-band facilities for Command Module and Lunar Excursion Module support; and an 85-foot diameter dish with one S-band system for lunar-range Apollo support.

In addition, Navy, Air Force, and NASA will team up to operate about five tracking ships.

Exciting, tense days are in store for all of us. Man's trip to the moon is just around the corner. But Apollo's astronauts would never dream of climbing into that spacecraft and blasting off into the unknown without the help and guidance of the terrenauts back on earth.

These men—the sky rangers of yesterday, today, and tomorrow, can feel proud of the role they play in pioneering the world beyond zero.

Bibliography

BOOKS

ALEXANDER, TOM. *Project Apollo.* New York, Harper and Row, 1964.

HAYES, E. NELSON. *The Smithsonian Satellite-Tracking Program: Its History and Organization.* Washington, D.C., Smithsonian Institution, Part I, Part II, 1962-1964.

HYNEK, ALLEN. *Exploring the Universe.* Columbus, Ohio, American Education Publications, 1961.

MACKO, STANLEY J. *Satellite Tracking.* New York, John F. Rider, Publisher, Inc., 1962.

STEHLING, KURT R. *Project Vanguard.* New York, Doubleday and Co., 1961.

ROSENTHAL, ALFRED. *The Early Years.* Goddard SPFC, NASA, 1964.

THOMAS, SHIRLEY. *Satellite Tracking Facilities.* New York, Holt, Rinehart and Winston, Inc., 1963.

MAGAZINES

Aviation Week and Space Technology, "NASA, Spearhead to Space." July 2, 1962.

Aviation Week and Space Technology, "SPASUR Now Giving Vital NORAD Coverage." November 26, 1962.

Life, "The Feat that Shook the Earth." October 21, 1957.

Life, "What Explorer is Telling Us." February 17, 1958.

TRAINER, JAMES. "Non-Nuclear Anti-Satellite Systems in Making." *Missiles and Rockets,* May 1964.

LaFOND, CHARLES. "Apollo Unified S-Band Network to Cost Minimum of $160-170 Million." *Missiles and Rockets,* July 20, 1964.

VAN ALLEN, JAMES. "The Artificial Satellite as a Research Instrument." *Scientific American,* November 1956.

HABER, HEINZ. "Space Satellites, Tools of Earth Research." *National Geographic,* April 1956.

FISHER, ALLAN C. "Exploring Tomorrow with the Space Agency." *National Geographic,* July 1960.

Think, A series of articles on the IGY. IBM Corporation, July 1957—December 1958.

PAPERS AND PERIODICALS

Air Defense Command Presentation for 9215th Air Reserve Squadron, New York City, 13, April 1964.

KOERNER, COL. E. "The U.S. Army and the IGY." *Army* Magazine, January 1957.

Boston Daily Globe, October 5, 1957.

Boston Herald, October 5, 1957.

JOYCE, DR. WALLACE J. "The Whole World a Laboratory." Address for IGY, January 28, 1957.

Goddard News, January 1963–May 1964.

MENGEL, JOHN T. "Satellite Ground Data Networks," a paper presented at the Northeast Electronics Research and Engineering Meeting, November 1963.

Interavia, "Satellite and Spacecraft Tracking." June 1963.

Parade, "Sky Spies." June 7, 1964.

WHIPPLE, F. L., AND HYNEK, J. A. "A Research Program Based on the Optical Tracking of Artificial Earth Satellites," presented March 20, 1956, at the IRE National Convention, New York, N.Y.

SAO News, Smithsonian Astrophysical Observatory, Cambridge, Mass., Vol. I, No. 1, June 1961, through Volume IV, No. 1, January 1964.

OTHER

Notes from the Station Chiefs' Conference Technical Sessions held in New Mexico, June 15-19, 1959.

Smithsonian Institution Astrophysical Observatory, Optical Satellite Tracking Program, carried out under a grant from NASA. Semiannual Progress Report No. 1-8.

INDEX

Index *

* Reference numbers in italics indicate illustrations.